W9-BRI-614

BOOK 1

PATTERNS IN SPELLING

Patterns with Short Vowels

TIM BROWN
DEBORAH F. KNIGHT

NEW READERS PRESS

About the Authors

Deborah Knight began her teaching career in the early 1970s and has taught both reading and English in urban, suburban, and rural settings. Since 1984, Ms. Knight has served as the Coordinator of the Learning Disabilities Assistance Program at Onondaga Community College in Syracuse, New York. Working closely with these OCC students, she has helped them to develop strategies for improving their reading, writing, spelling, and study skills.

Tim Brown has worked with developing and remedial readers and writers since 1978. He has taught courses in spelling as well as freshman composition and literature at Onondaga Community College. He has also served as Senior Professional Tutor at the college's Writing Skills Center, where he has had a special interest in teaching spelling to developing and remedial writers and ESL students.

ON THE COVER: A quilt entitled *Rhythm/Color: Morris Men;* 99½" x 99½", by Michael James. This work of art appeared in *The Art Quilt* exhibit and book of the same name. It is reproduced here through the courtesy of The Quilt Digest Press.

Patterns in Spelling
ISBN 978-0-88336-100-9

Copyright © 1990 New Readers Press
New Readers Press
ProLiteracy's Publishing Division
104 Marcellus Street, Syracuse, New York 13204
www.newreaderspress.com

All rights reserved. No part of this book may be reproduced or transmitted in any form or by any means, electronic or mechanical, including photocopying, recording, or by any information storage and retrieval system, without permission in writing from the publisher.

Printed in the United States of America
20 19 18

Proceeds from the sale of New Readers Press materials support professional development, training, and technical assistance programs of ProLiteracy that benefit local literacy programs in the U.S. and around the globe.

Project Editor: Christina M. Jagger
Manuscript Editor: Mary Hutchison
Illustrations: Joe Glisson
Cover: Chris Steenwerth
Composition: Anne Hyde

Table of Contents

Readiness Lesson

1 **The Alphabet.** Write the alphabet on the lines below.

S T W U Y Z
S W U Y Z
T W U Y Z

A B C D E F G H I J K L M N O P Q R S T U V W X Y Z

2 **Vowels.** On the line below, write the letters of the alphabet that are vowels.

A O U E   A E I U

3 **Hearing Syllables in Words.** Write the number of syllables you hear in each word.

1. 2
2. 2
3. 2
4. 3
5. 2

6. 3
7. 3
8. 2
9. 2
10. 3

4 **Hearing Sounds in Words.** Write the number of sounds you hear in each word.

1. 2
2. 3
3. 2
4. 3
5.

6.
7.
8.
9.
10.

5 **Hearing the Beginnings of Words.** Write the letter for the first sound you hear in each word.

1. _D_
2. _S_
3. _W_
4. _F_
5. _F_

6. _C_
7. _G_
8. _____
9. _____
10. _____

6 **Hearing the Ends of Words.** Write the letter for the last sound you hear in each word.

1. _m_
2. _p_
3. _t_
4. _g_
5. _S_

6. _K_
7. _S_
8. _____
9. _____
10. _____

7 **Rhyming.** Say the name of each of these pairs of objects aloud. If the two words rhyme, place an **X** on the line provided.

1. _X_

2. _X_

3.

4. 

5.  

6.  

7.  

8.

8 **More Rhyming.** Write a word which rhymes with each word given.

1. bill ~~Hell~~ hill

2. big ~~Hell~~ ~~big~~ dig

3. nut But

4. hit Bit

5. fun run

6. tell ~~Big~~ well

7. ten men

8. lock clok

9. rod tod

10. bat cat

9 **Word Building.** Write as many words as you can think of which rhyme with sit.

Hit

Iit

Lit

Fit

pit

kit

Lesson 1

The Word Families *ig*, *ib*, and *in*

Sight Words			
one	three	is	the
two	four	are	

Word Families

ig

ib

in

① Listening

Listen to the sound *ig* makes in these words.

big	pig
dig	wig
rig	biggest

Listen to the sound *ib* makes in these words.

bib
rib
sibling

Listen to the sound *in* makes in these words.

fin
pin
tin
chin

2 **Word Building.** Fill in the missing letters.

p _i_ _g_   _p_ ig

ch _i_ _n_   _c_ _h_ in

f _i_ _n_   _f_ in

3 **Writing Words.** On the lines below, write the words that you hear.

1. wig   4. Big   7. three
2. big   5. pig   8. four
3. rib   6. bid   9. is

4 **Writing Numbers.** Write the word for each number on the line beside it.

1 fin   2 pin   3 tin   4 chin

5 **The Ending -s.** If you have <u>more than one</u> person, place, or thing, add an *-s* to the end of the word to make it plural.

Example: one pig   two pigs

Write the number and the name of the things in the pictures. The first one has been done to get you started. Do the rest by yourself. Remember to add an *-s* if you have more than one.

two pigs

Chins three

one fin

four bibs

three pins

~~tow~~ *Wigs*
two

6 **Writing Sentences.** On the lines below, write the sentences that you hear.

1. _____

2. _____

3. _____

4. _____

5. _____

6. _____

Lesson 2

The Word Families *ip*, *im*, and *it*

Sight Words				
five	seven	be	was	he
six	eight	am	were	she

Word Families

ip

im

it

1 **Listening**

Listen to the sound *ip* makes in these words.

dip	rip	chip
hip	tip	ship
lip	zip	

Listen to the sound *im* makes in these words.

dim
him
Jim

Listen to the sound *it* makes in these words.

bit	fit
hit	limit
sit	

2 **Word Building.** Fill in the missing letters.

     h _i_ _p_   _h_ ip

   sh _i_ _p_   _S_ _h_ ip

   l _i_ _p_ _s_   _l_ ips

     s _i_ _t_   _S_ it

     r _i_ _p_   _r_ ip

3 **Writing Words.** On the lines below, write the words that you hear.

1. _____   5. _____   9. _____
2. _____   6. _____   10. _____
3. _____   7. _____   11. _____
4. _____   8. _____   12. _____

4 **Writing Numbers.** Write the word for each number on the line beside it.

5 _fire_   6 _six_   7 _seven_   8 _eight_

5 **Word Building.** Think of as many words as you can that end with the *it* family. Write the words below.

b it   lim it   _____ it
s it   f it   _____ it
h it   _____ it   _____ it

6 **Dictionary Skills: Alphabetizing.** Write the words below on index cards or small pieces of paper. Then put the words in alphabetical order.

rib	him	sibling
fin	limit	chin
big	zip	tip

7 **The Ending -s.** Make the following words plural (more than one thing) by adding -s. The first one has been done to get you started.

1. hip + s _hips_

2. trip + s _tris_

3. lip + s _lips_

4. ship + s _ships_

5. visit + s _risit_

6. bit + s _bits_

7. tip + s _tips_

8. rip + s _rips_

8 **Writing Sentences.** On the lines below, write the sentences that you hear.

1. _____

2. _____

3. _____

4. _____

5. _____

6. _____

7. _____

8. _____

Lesson 3

The Word Families *is*, *id*, and *ick*

Sight Words				
nine	eleven	me	you	her
ten	twelve	we	they	

Word Families

is

id

ick

1 Listening

Listen to the sounds *is* makes in these words.

is	this
his	sister
visit	

Listen to the sound *id* makes in these words.

bid	kid
did	lid
hid	rid

Listen to the sound *ick* makes in these words.

pick
sick
tick
thick
chicken

2 **Word Building.** Fill in the missing letters.

l _i d_   _L_ id

ch _i c k_ en   _c h_ ick _e n_

k _i d_   _K_ id

s _i s_ ters   _s_ is _t e r s_

is, id, ick

3 **Word Building.** Add *is*, *id*, or *ick* to each of the letters below to make a word. Do not make the same word twice. The first one has been done to get you started.

1. b _id_
2. h _ick_
3. h _is_
4. h _id_
5. k _ick_

6. k _id_
7. l _id_
8. l _ick_
9. p _ick_
10. r _id_

11. s _ister_
12. t _ick_
13. ch _icken_
14. th _ick_
15. th _is_

4 **Writing Words.** On the lines below, write the words that you hear.

1. _____
2. _____
3. _____
4. _____

5. _____
6. _____
7. _____
8. _____

9. _____
10. _____
11. _____
12. _____

5 **Writing Numbers.** Write the word for each number on the line beside it.

2 _two_
7 _seven_
12 _twelve_
5 _five_

9 _nine_
11 _eleven_
3 _three_
6 _six_

1 _one_
4 _four_
10 _ten_
8 _eight_

6 **Dictionary Skills: Alphabetizing.** Write the words below on index cards or pieces of paper. Then put the words in alphabetical order.

visit	is
chicken	pick
this	hid
did	sick
bid	lid

7 **The Ending -s.** Add -s to action words if a *he*, a *she*, or an *it* is doing the action. Do not add -s when *I, you, we,* or *they* are doing the action. Study the sentences below.

He kicks.	Nick kicks.	I kick.
She kicks.	Kim kicks.	You kick.
It kicks.	The horse kicks.	We kick.
		They kick.

Choose one of the words below to put in each sentence. Add -s to the word because a he, a she, or an it is doing the acting in each sentence.

~~dip~~   ~~fit~~   ~~pick~~   visit

1. She _dips_ the chips.
2. Kim _picks_ the big ring.
3. The ring _fits_ her finger.
4. The boy _visits_ his sick sister.

8 **Writing Sentences.** On the lines below, write the sentences that you hear.

1. _Tim is Eleven._
2. _Dick Picks You._
3. _We hid twelve Pins._
4. _She bit her Lip._
5. _____
6. _____
7. _____
8. _____

Lesson 4

The Word Families *ich*, *itch*, *ix*, and *ish*

Sight Words		
by	do	of
for	does	with
and	who	under

Word Families

ich

itch

ix

ish

1 **Listening**

Listen to the sound *ich* makes in these words.

    rich
    which
   sandwich

Listen to the sound *itch* makes in these words.

ditch	itch	kitchen
pitch	stitch	
witch	switch	

Listen to the sound *ix* makes in these words.

    fix
    mix
    six

Listen to the sound *ish* makes in these words.

dish	fishing
fish	wishes
wish	finish

2 **Word Building.** Add either *ich*, *itch*, *ix*, or *ish* to each of the letters below to make a word. Do not make the same word twice.

1. d_ish_   4. f_ishing_   7. s_ix_
2. d_itch_   5. m_ix_   8. sw_itch_
3. f_ix_   6. r_ich_   9. sw_ish_

3 **Writing Words.** On the lines below, write the words that you hear.

1. _rich_   5. _six_   9. _itch_
2. _ditch_   6. _mix_   10. _kitchen_
3. _fish_   7. _fishing_   11. _which_
4. _wish_   8. _switch_   12. _witch_

4 **Dictionary Skills: Alphabetizing.** Write the words in the first two columns of Exercise 3 on index cards or pieces of paper. Put the words in alphabetical order.

5 **The Ending -es.** If a word ends in *s*, *x*, *z*, *ch*, or *sh*, add *-es* instead of *-s*.

Add *-es* to the words in parentheses, and write them in the blanks.

1. (ditch)   He digs _ditches_ .
2. (itch)   Her skin _itches_ .
3. (witch)   The three _witches_ hid the ring.
4. (rich)   In the story, she gives her _riches_ to him.

6 **The Endings -s and -es.** Add -s or -es to the words in parentheses, and write them in the blanks. Remember to add -es if the word ends in s, x, z, ch, or sh.

1. (pitch)   Jim _Pitches_ to us.

2. (ditch)   Mitch digs _ditches_.

3. (pin)   Who has the _Pins_?

4. (kitchen)   The _Kitchens_ are big.

5. (wish)   — Kip has three _Wishs_   wishes

6. (wig)   ⇀ Kim has four of the _wigs_.

7. (pig)   ⇀ This is the man who has two _Pigs_.   sp

8. (stitch)   ⇀ Dick had twelve _Stitches_ in his chin.

9. (mix)   ⇀ She _Mixes_ the big chips with the little ones.

7 **Which or Witch.** Read the two sentences below.

Sentence 1:   Who is a <u>witch</u>?
Sentence 2:   <u>Which</u> girl is biggest?

Now use *which* or *witch* to complete the sentences below.

1. _Which_ pig is his?

2. The _Witch_ is in the kitchen.

3. _Which_ ship comes at six?

4. The _Witch_ is fixing her sandwiches.

8 **The Endings -s and -es.** Write the number and the name of the things in the pictures. Remember to add *-s* or *-es*.

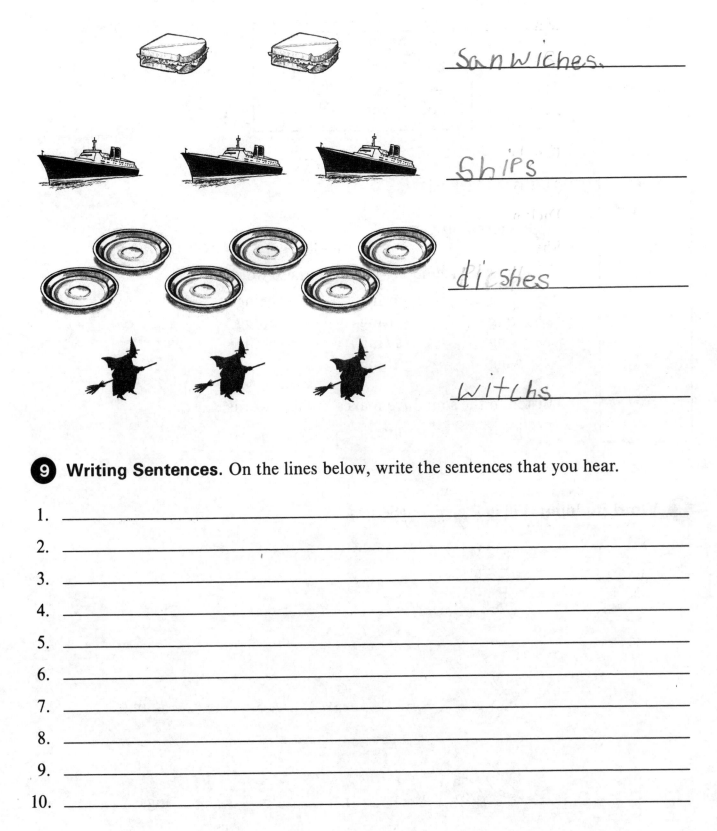

Sanwiches.

Ships

dishes

witchs

9 **Writing Sentences.** On the lines below, write the sentences that you hear.

1. _____
2. _____
3. _____
4. _____
5. _____
6. _____
7. _____
8. _____
9. _____
10. _____

Lesson 5

The Word Families *ing* and *ive*

Sight Words

no	or	could
so	but	come
go	yet	

Word Families

ing

ive

1 Listening

Listen to the sound *ing* makes in these words.

king	bring	being
ring	sting	doing
sing	swing	going
wing	thing	

Listen to the sound *ive* makes in these words.

give   live

2 Word Building. Fill in the missing letters.

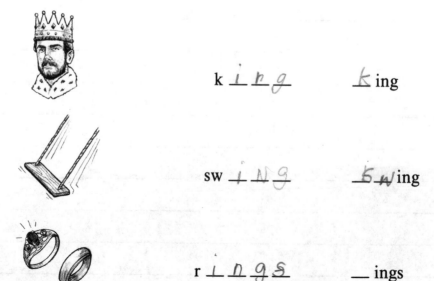

k i n g   k ing

sw i n g   s w ing

r i n g s   __ ings

3 **Writing Words.** On the lines below, write the words that you hear.

1. _____   5. _____   9. _____

2. _____   6. _____   10. _____

3. _____   7. _____   11. _____

4. _____   8. _____   12. _____

4 **Hearing Syllables.** Read the words below out loud. On the line beside each word, write the number of syllables in the word.

1. cat   _1__   5. visit _2__   9. sibling _2__

2. chicken _2__   6. this   _1__   10. limit   _1__

3. go   _1__   7. bib   _1__   11. chips   _1__

4. goes   ____   8. pin   _1__   12. finish _2__

5 **One-One-One Words.** One-one-one words have *one* syllable, *one* vowel, and end in *one* consonant.

On the line below, write the letters of the alphabet which are vowels.

_____

Put an **X** beside each word below which has one syllable, one vowel, and ends in one consonant.

1. dig   __X__   5. limit _____   9. zip   __X__

2. chin __X__   6. thick __X__   10. pick   __X__

3. visit _____   7. pin   __X__   11. finish _____

4. hit   __X__   8. fish   __X__   12. chip   __X__

A, e, i, o, u,   Sometimes
                 w & y

Lesson 5   25

6 **Adding the Ending -*ing* to One-One-One Words**

Pattern: If you have a word which has <u>one</u> syllable, <u>one</u> vowel, and ends in <u>one</u> consonant, double the last consonant before adding -*ing*.

Add -*ing* to the words below. The first one has been done to get you started.

1. dig + ing   _digging_

2. pin + ing   _PINNING_

3. hit + ing   _hitting_

4. ship + ing   _shipping_

5. tip + ing   _tipping_

6. dim + ing   _dimming_

7 **More Practice with Adding -*ing***

Pattern: Do not double the final consonant if the <u>word ends in more than one consonant</u> or <u>in a vowel</u>. Do not double <u>w</u> or <u>x</u>.

Look at each word below. If the word has *one* syllable, *one* vowel, or *one* final consonant, check the appropriate box. If you check all three boxes, double the final consonant and add -*ing* unless the word ends in <u>w or x</u>. If you do not check all three boxes, just add -*ing*. The first one has been done to get you started.

	One syllable	One vowel	One final consonant		
1. hit	✓	✓	✓	+ ing	_hitting_
2. pick	✓	✓		+ ing	_picking_
3. chin	✓	✓		+ ing	_chinning_
4. finish	✓	✓	✓	+ ing	_finishing_
5. kid	✓	✓		+ ing	_kidding_
6. go	✓	✓		+ ing	_going_
7. fix		✓		+ ing	_fixing_
8. rip	✓	✓	✓	+ ing	_ripping_

8 **Still More Practice with Adding -ing.** Add -ing to the words below. Double the final consonant if the word has *one* syllable, *one* vowel, and *one* final consonant. Do not double *w* or *x*.

1. pitch + ing _Pitch ing_

2. mix + ing _miking_

3. do + ing _do ing_

4. zip + ing _ziping_

5. dip + ing _diping_

6. itch + ing _Itching_

7. dim + ing _dimming_

8. sit + ing _Sitting_

9. chip + ing _chiping_

10. stitch + ing _stitching_

11. wish + ing _wishing_

12. rip + ing _ripping_

13. chin + ing _Chining_

14. kid + ing _Kiding_

9 **Writing Sentences.** On the lines below, write the sentences that you hear.

1. _____

2. _____

3. _____

4. _____

5. _____

6. _____

7. _____

8. _____

_____

Lesson 6

The Word Families *iss*, *iff*, and *ill*

```
┌─────────────────────────────────┐
│          Sight Words            │
│   if     want     have          │
│   to     your     some          │
└─────────────────────────────────┘
```

Word Families
iss
iff
ill

❶ Listening

Listen to the sound *iss* makes in these words.

kiss   missing

miss   dismiss

Listen to the sound *iff* makes in these words.

cliff   stiff

Listen to the sound *ill* makes in these words.

bill
fill
hill
still

❷ Word Building. Think of as many words as you can that have the *ill* family in them. Write them below.

bill ___ill   ch ___ill   L ___ill

fill ___ill   k ___ill   J ___ill

still ___ill   P ___ill   W ___ill

3 **Writing Words.** On the lines below, write the words that you hear.

1. _____   8. _____   15. _____

2. _____   9. _____   16. _____

3. _____   10. _____   17. _____

4. _____   11. _____   18. _____

5. _____   12. _____   19. _____

6. _____   13. _____   20. _____

7. _____   14. _____   21. _____

4 **Finding a Pattern.** Look at the words in Exercise 1. Then fill in the blanks in the sentences below to find a spelling pattern.

1. When one-syllable words with a short vowel end with the sound /f/, the final sound is usually spelled __ __.

2. When one-syllable words with a short vowel end with the sound /l/, the final sound is usually spelled __ __.

3. When one-syllable words with a short vowel end with the sound /s/, the final sound is usually spelled __ __.

5 **Dictionary Skills: Alphabetizing.** Write the words your teacher dictates to you on index cards or pieces of paper. Alphabetize the words. Then copy the words in alphabetical order on the lines below.

1. _____   4. _____   7. _____

2. _____   5. _____   8. _____

3. _____   6. _____   9. _____

6 **Dictionary Skills: Getting to Know the Dictionary.** Find the page in your dictionary where words starting with the letter *a* begin. Write the number of the page after the letter *A* below. Do this for each of the other letters.

A _1_   L _404_   S _637_

F _266_   R _593_   X _846_

Now fill in the blanks in the sentences below.

1. The letter _S_ has the most words.

2. The letter _X_ has the fewest words.

3. How many words appear at the top of each dictionary page? _2_

4. Why do you think those words appear at the top of each page? _____

_____

7 **Dictionary Skills: Locating Words.** Find each of the words below in your dictionary. Write the number of the page on which you find each word on the line beside the word.

1. baby _____   4. fable _____   7. rabbit _____

2. cab _____   5. jack _____   8. table _____

3. dab _____   6. machine _____   9. zap _____

8 **The Ending -*ing*.** Add -*ing* to the words below. Double the final consonant when you need to. Write the new words on the lines provided.

1. pin _pinning_   5. pick _pick_

2. fit _fitting_   6. chip _chipping_

3. kid _kidding_   7. fill _filling_

4. dig _diging_   8. itch _itching_

30   Lesson 6

9 **Writing Sentences.** On the lines below, write the sentences that you hear.

1. _____

2. _____

3. _____

4. _____

5. _____

6. _____

10 **Crossword Puzzle.** Use the clues below to complete the crossword puzzle with word family words you have learned so far. If you get stumped, check the list of words below.

Across

1. They sail the seas.
3. I didn't mean it; I was only ____.
6. They swim in the sea.
7. It lays eggs.
8. My mother's other daughter
9. Make music with your voice

Down

1. If in time, these save nine.
2. A brother or sister
4. The teacher will ____ the class.
5. Makes a present of; donates
6. End
7. The bottom of your face

Word List: chin fish gives ships sing stitches
chicken dismiss finish kidding sister sibling

Review of Unit 1

The Short *i*

1 **Hearing Syllables.** Read the words below out loud. On the line beside each word, write the number of syllables in the word.

1. pig _____1_____   5. sandwich __2__   9. hip _____1_____

2. biggest __2__   6. nip _____1_____   10. fishing __2__

3. tick _____1_____   7. lid _____1_____   11. doing __2__

4. switch _____1_____   8. kitchen __2__   12. visit __2__

2 **Dictionary Skills: Alphabetizing.** Alphabetize the words in Exercise 1.

1. _____   5. _____   9. _____

2. _____   6. _____   10. _____

3. _____   7. _____   11. _____

4. _____   8. _____   12. _____

3 **Word Building.** Add one of the word families listed below to each of the letters to make a word. Do not make the same word twice.

ig	ip	is	ich	ish	iss
ib	im	id	itch	ing	iff
in	it	ick	ix	ive	ill

1. b _ig___   8. p_____   15. ch_____

2. d _oing___   9. r_____   16. cr_____

3. f _ishing___   10. s_____   17. sh_____

4. h _ill___   11. t_____   18. sp_____

5. k _ing___   12. w_____   19. st_____

6. l _id___   13. z_____   20. sw_____

7. m _ill___   14. br_____   21. th_____

4 **Using Words.** Fill in the blanks in the story with one of the words listed below. Use each word only once. The first one has been done to get you started.

are	eight	fishing	still	✓ visits
by	finishes	fix	this	wishes
dishes	fish	kitchen	under	with

Chip, who is ten, ___Visits___ his dad on weekends. He wants to go fishing

_____ weekend. His dad would like to go _____, too. His

dad _____ working at five. They eat supper in the _____, do

the _____, and are in bed _____ nine. The next morning they

_____ at the lake by seven o'clock. Chip sits _____. He

gets _____ fish. Five _____ are big. Three fish are

_____ the limit. When they get home, they _____ the fish for

dinner. Chip loves to fish _____ his dad. He _____ they could

fish every weekend.

5 **Creating Sentences.** On the lines below, write one sentence about each picture.

1.

2.

1. _____

_____

2. _____

_____

6 Patterns for Adding Endings

Pattern: If you have more than one person, place, or thing, add *-s* to the end of the word to make it plural.

Add *-s* to the words below and read each word.

1. fin   _fins_

2. rip   _rips_

3. wing   _wings_

4. bill   _bills_

Pattern: Add *-s* to action words if a he, a she, or an it is doing the action.

Add *-s* to the words below and read each word.

1. kick   _kicks_

2. come   _comes_

3. give   _gives_

4. fit   _fits_

5. tip   _Tips_

6. sit   _sits_

Pattern: If a word ends in *s, x, z, ch,* or *sh,* add *-es.*

Add *-es* to the words below and read each word.

1. mix   _mixes_

2. wish   _wishes_

3. rich   _riches_

4. ditch   _ditches_

5. stitch   _stitches_

6. dish   _dishes_

Add *-s* or *-es* to the words below and read each word.

1. wig   _wigs_

2. fix   _fixes_

3. pitch   _pitches_

4. swing   _swinges_

5. itch   _itches_

6. ship   _ships_

Pattern: If you have a word which has one syllable, one vowel, and one final consonant, double the last consonant before adding -*ing*. Do not double *w* or *x*.

Add -*ing* to the words below and read each word.

1. hit _____   7. string _____

2. fix _____   8. tip _____

3. go _____   9. limit _____

4. itch _____   10. dig _____

5. chip _____   11. rip _____

6. dim _____   12. sing _____

7 **Writing Sentences.** On the lines below, write the sentences that you hear.

1. _____

2. _____

3. _____

4. _____

5. _____

6. _____

7. _____

8. _____

9. _____

10. _____

Lesson 7

The Word Families *ut*, *um*, and *up*

Sight Words		
what	would	says
where	should	once

Word Families

1 **Listening**

ut

Listen to the sound *ut* makes in these words.

but	gut	cut
hut	nut	cutting
rut	shut	

um

Listen to the sound *um* makes in these words.

gum	sum	number

up

Listen to the sound *up* makes in these words.

up	pups
cup	upset

2 **Word Building.** Fill in the missing letters.

c __ __   __ up

g __ __   __ um

n __ __ bers   __ um __ __ __ s

3 **Writing Words.** On the lines below, write the words that you hear.

1. _____   4. _____   7. _____

2. _____   5. _____   8. _____

3. _____   6. _____   9. _____

4 **Hearing Syllables.** Read the words below out loud. On the line beside
each word, write the number of syllables in the word.

1. but _____   4. upon _____   7. jump _____   10. summer _____

2. gutting _____   5. number _____   8. limiting _____   11. jumps _____

3. shut _____   6. pups _____   9. hut _____   12. once _____

5 **One-One-One Words.** One-one-one words have *one* syllable, *one*
vowel, and end in *one* consonant.

On the line below, write the letters of the alphabet which are vowels.

_____

Put an **X** beside each word below which has one syllable, one vowel, and ends in one
consonant.

1. cut _____   5. butter _____   9. jump _____

2. sum _____   6. shut _____   10. number _____

3. fish _____   7. dig _____   11. chip _____

4. pick _____   8. switch _____   12. give _____

6 Adding the Ending -ed to One-One-One Words

Pattern: If you have a word which has *one* syllable, *one* vowel, and ends in *one* consonant, double the last consonant before adding -ed.

Add -ed to the words below.

1. sum + ed _____

2. ship + ed _____

3. tip + ed _____

4. drum + ed _____

5. pin + ed _____

6. zip + ed _____

7 More Practice with Adding -ed

Pattern: Do not double the final consonant before adding -ed if the word ends in more than one consonant or in a vowel. Do not double *w* or *x*.

Look at each word below. If the word has one syllable, one vowel, or one final consonant, check the appropriate box. If you check all three boxes, double the final consonant and add -ed unless the word ends in *w* or *x*. If you do not check all three boxes, just add -ed.

	One syllable	One vowel	One final consonant		
1. tip				+ ed	_____
2. drum				+ ed	_____
3. rip				+ ed	_____
4. fish				+ ed	_____
5. jump				+ ed	_____
6. cup				+ ed	_____
7. fix				+ ed	_____
8. butter				+ ed	_____

8 **The Endings -*ed* and -*ing*.** Fill in the correct answer in each statement below.

1. The ending -*ed* begins with a _____. (consonant, vowel)

2. The ending -*ing* begins with a _____. (consonant, vowel)

9 **Doubling Pattern 1.** Fill in the blanks in the sentence below to state a pattern.

Double the final consonant if the word has _____ syllable, _____ vowel, and _____ final consonant, and the ending begins with a _____.

Add -*ing* or -*ed* to the words below. Use Doubling Pattern 1 which you just wrote. Do not double *w* or *x*.

1. cut + ing   _____

2. number + ed _____

3. fish + ing   _____

4. dip + ed   _____

5. lump + ed _____

6. fix + ed   _____

7. dim + ed   _____

8. kill + ed   _____

10 **Writing Sentences.** On the lines below, write the sentences that you hear.

1. _____

2. _____

3. _____

4. _____

5. _____

6. _____

7. _____

8. _____

9. _____

10. _____

Lesson 8

The Word Families *un*, *ub*, and *us*

Sight Words		
said	put	none
only	goes	done

Word Families

1 Listening

un

Listen to the sound *un* makes in these words.

fun	until	begun
run	bunch	under
sun	lunch	thunder

ub

Listen to the sound *ub* makes in these words.

cub	tub
pub	rub
public	rubber

us

Listen to the sound *us* makes in these words.

us	dust
bus	just
thus	must

2 Writing Words. On the lines below, write the words that you hear.

1. _____   4. _____   7. _____

2. _____   5. _____   8. _____

3. _____   6. _____   9. _____

3 Doubling Pattern 1. Fill in the blanks in the sentences below to review Doubling Pattern 1.

Double the final consonant if the word has _____ syllable, _____ vowel, and

_____ final consonant, and the ending begins with a _____. Do *not*

double these two consonants: _____.

4 The Ending -*er*. Fill in the blank in the sentence below.

The ending -*er* begins with a _____. (vowel, consonant)

Add -*er* to the words below. Use Doubling Pattern 1.

1. rub + er   _____
2. drum + er   _____

3. zip + er   _____
4. sting + er _____

5 Adding Endings. Add -*er*, -*ed*, or -*ing* to these words. Double the consonant when you should.

1. slip + ed   _____
2. swim + ing   _____
3. hunt + er   _____
4. sing + er   _____

5. mix + er   _____
6. rub + ed   _____
7. drum + ed   _____
8. jump + ing   _____

6 A Pattern with Meaning: -*er*.

Part A. Read the words below. Then write the root word (base word) for each word on the line to the right.

1. swimmer _____
2. kisser _____
3. drummer _____

4. hunter _____
5. mixer _____
6. zipper _____

Part B. Fill in the blanks in the sentences below to find a meaning pattern for *-er*.

1. A swimmer is _____ who swims.

2. A drummer is _____ who drums.

3. A zipper is _____ that zips.

Write the meaning of *-er* on the line below.

_____

7 **A Pattern with Meaning: *un-*.** Read the words below. Then write the root word (base word) for each word on the line to the right.

1. undo _____   3. untie _____   5. unsaid _____

2. unmake _____   4. unhitch _____   6. unpin _____

In these words *un-* means "the reverse of." Now write sentences using the words below.

1. undo _____

2. untie _____

3. unhitch _____

8 **Dictionary Skills: Alphabetizing.** Write the words below in alphabetical order on the lines provided.

bus   1. _____

begun   2. _____

bill   3. _____

brick   4. _____

by   5. _____

9 **The Possessive Apostrophe.** When something belongs to someone or something else, use an *'s* to show this possession.

Examples: Bob's cup   the kid's sandwich
         the nut's shell   the pig's dish

Rewrite the phrases below using an *'s* to show possession. The first one has been done to get you started.

1. the wish of Jim   *Jim's wish*

2. the pig of the man _____

3. the itch of Sid   _____

4. the rig of the ship _____

5. the three chins of Bill _____

10 **Writing Sentences.** On the lines below, write the sentences that you hear.

1. _____

2. _____

3. _____

4. _____

5. _____

6. _____

7. _____

8. _____

9. _____

10. _____

Lesson 9

The Word Families *ud*, *ug*, and *uck*

Sight Words		
too	again	buy
any	against	laugh

Word Families

ud

ug

uck

1 Listening

Listen to the sound *ud* makes in these words.

bud	study	cuddle
mud	sudden	huddle

Listen to the sound *ug* makes in these words.

bug	dug	juggle
ugly	drug	snuggle

Listen to the sound *uck* makes in these words.

duck	luck	stuck
buck	tuck	struck
buckle	truck	

2 Writing Words. On the lines below, write the words that you hear.

1. _____
2. _____
3. _____
4. _____

5. _____
6. _____
7. _____
8. _____

9. _____
10. _____
11. _____
12. _____

3 **Dictionary Skills: The Schwa**. The dictionary tells us how words are pronounced. The pronunciation of a word is usually found beside the entry word. Certain symbols show us how to pronounce the word.

The schwa represents the short vowel sound in most unaccented syllables. For instance, it is the sound made by the first *a* in *again* and *against*. This sound can be spelled many ways.

Many dictionaries use an upside down *e* (ə) as the symbol for the schwa when they show how to pronounce a word.

To see if your dictionary uses the schwa, look up the word *snuggle*. If the schwa is used, it will show the pronunciation of *snuggle* as *(snŭgˊəl)*.

Look up the words below in the dictionary. If the dictionary shows a schwa in the unaccented syllable, underline the word.

buckle   chicken   huddle   juggle   kitchen

4 **Finding a Pattern**. Write the words that you hear. Then say the second syllable of each word.

1. _____   3. _____   5. _____

2. _____   4. _____

What two letters are used to spell the /əl/ sound following a consonant? ___ ___

> **Pattern:** The letters *le* are usually used to spell the sound /əl/ following a consonant.

5 **Finding Another Pattern**. Write the words you hear.

1. _____   2. _____   3. _____

What two letters are used to spell the sound /k/? ___ ___

Where are these two letters found in the word? _____

> **Pattern:** The letters *ck* are usually used to spell the sound /k/ at the end of a one-syllable word.

6 **Dictionary Skills: Alphabetizing.** Write the words below in alphabetical order on the lines provided.

jug
drug
stuck
duck
cuddle
dug
struck
bug

1. _____   5. _____

2. _____   6. _____

3. _____   7. _____

4. _____   8. _____

7 **The Endings -*ing* and -*ed*.** Choose one of the words below to put in each sentence. Add either -*ing* or -*ed* to each word.

bud   finish   laugh   pitch   visit

1. Jud _____ the ball.

2. The rosebush was _____.

3. Jill _____ at her sister.

4. She is _____ her homework.

5. Her sister is _____ her for three weeks.

8 ***Too* or *Two*.** Read the six sentences below.

1. I have two sisters.   3. Jim wants too many things.   5. Her mother is fat, too.
2. Bill read two books.   4. She is too fat.   6. I want to go, too.

Fill in the blanks below with *too* or *two*. Then write the correct definition for your choice in the space provided.

1. I saw _____ chicks.   Definition: _____

2. The ground is _____ muddy.   Definition: _____

3. I caught _____ fish.   Definition: _____

4. One fish is _____ small.   Definition: _____

5. Bill is a juggler and Sid is, _____.   Definition: _____

9 *Buy* **or** *By*. Read the four sentences below.

1. She will buy new shoes.
2. I want to buy some gum.
3. The bus stopped by the ditch.
4. I will go by my mom's house.

Fill in the blanks below with *buy* or *by*. Then write the correct definition for your choice in the space provided.

1. The duck is _____ the lake.   Definition: _____

2. I must _____ three books for the kids.   Definition: _____

3. I will _____ that buckle.   Definition: _____

4. When I jog, I go _____ her house.   Definition: _____

10 **Writing Sentences.** On the lines below, write the sentences that you hear.

1. _____
2. _____
3. _____
4. _____
5. _____
6. _____
7. _____
8. _____

Lesson 10

The Word Families *uss*, *uff*, and *ull*

Sight Words		
about	eye	that
love	little	there

Word Families

1 **Listening**

uss

Listen to the sound *uss* makes in these words.

fuss	cuss
muss	discuss

uff

Listen to the sound *uff* makes in these words.

cuff	bluff	muffin
huff	scuff	buffalo
puff	stuff	

ull

Listen to the sound *ull* makes in these words.

dull	mull
gull	skull
lull	

2 **Word Building.** Add either *uss*, *uff*, or *ull* to each of the letters below to make a word. Do not make the same word twice.

1. c _____   5. g _____   9. bl _____

2. c _____   6. h _____   10. sc _____

3. d _____   7. m _____   11. sk _____

4. f _____   8. m _____   12. st _____

3 **Writing Words.** On the lines below, write the words that you hear.

1. _____   5. _____   9. _____

2. _____   6. _____   10. _____

3. _____   7. _____   11. _____

4. _____   8. _____   12. _____

4 **Rediscovering a Pattern.** Look at the words in Exercise 3. Then fill in the blanks in the sentence below.

When one-syllable words with a short vowel end with the sound /f/, /l/,

or /s/, the final sounds are usually spelled __ __, __ __, or __ __.

5 **Adding -s or -es to Action Words.** Choose one of the words below to put in each sentence. Add -s or -es to the word because a he, a she, or an it is doing the acting in each sentence.

discuss   fuss   huff   lull   scuff

1. Chuck _____ his shoes.

2. Bill _____ when he runs.

3. The baby _____ until 2 a.m.

4. Jill _____ the baby to sleep.

5. The teacher _____ the problem.

6 **Using Pronouns.** Use the pronouns *she, we,* or *me* to fill in the blanks in the sentences below.

1. _____ goes to school with _____.

2. _____ bakes muffins every week.

3. _____ huff and puff at the gym.

4. _____ go to the zoo to see the buffalo.

5. _____ discusses the story with _____.

7 **The Ending 's.** Rewrite the phrases below using an *'s* to show possession. See Exercise 9 in Lesson 8 if you have forgotten how to do this.

1. the cuff of the shirt _____

2. the skull of the buffalo _____

3. the bluff of Buck _____

4. the ring of the king _____

5. the love of Tim _____

8 **Using the Dictionary.** Find the page where words beginning with the following letters first appear in your dictionary. Write the number of the page on the line.

C _____   H _____   P _____

E _____   K _____   T _____

G _____   N _____   Y _____

9 **Creating Sentences.** Write a sentence using some form of each word below.

1. puff _____

_____

2. dull _____

_____

3. skull _____

_____

4. love _____

_____

5. fuss _____

_____

10 **Writing Sentences.** On the lines below, write the sentences that you hear.

1. _____
2. _____
3. _____
4. _____
5. _____
6. _____
7. _____
8. _____

Lesson 11

The Word Families *ush*, *unk*, *ung*, and *udge*

Sight Words		
gone	pull	shoe
shall	full	whom

Word Families

1 Listening

ush

Listen to the sound *ush* makes in these words.

gush	mush
hush	blush
rush	usher

unk

Listen to the sound *unk* makes in these words.

dunk	chunk
junk	drunk
sunk	trunk

ung

Listen to the sound *ung* makes in these words.

lung	hung
rung	hunger
sung	

udge

Listen to the sound *udge* makes in these words.

fudge	budge
judge	nudge

2 **Writing Words.** On the lines below, write the words that you hear.

1. _____   4. _____

2. _____   5. _____

3. _____   6. _____

3 **Word Building.** Add *ush*, *unk*, *ung*, or *udge* to each of the letters below to make a word. Do not make the same word twice.

1. bl _____   5. fl _____   9. st _____

2. br _____   6. fl _____   10. st _____

3. cl _____   7. gr _____   11. tr _____

4. dr _____   8. pl _____   12. tr _____

4 **Using Words.** Fill in the blanks with one of the words below. Use each word only once.

budge	mud	shall	stuck
could	pulled	shoes	sunk
full	said	struck	trunk

A ship had _____ a rock and _____. Jim and Tim could

see a trunk _____ in the _____. "_____ I dive for

it?" asked Jim. Tim _____ that he should. Jim reached the trunk, but

he _____ not _____ it. Then Tim went down to help him.

They _____ the _____ out of the mud and opened it. It

was _____ of _____.

5 **Finding a Pattern.** On the lines below, write the words that you hear.

1. _____   4. _____

2. _____   5. _____

3. _____   6. _____

The /u/ in these words is called a short *u*. Write the letters that say /uj/. _____

What letters spell /j/ after a short *u*? _____

   Pattern: The letters *dge* spell /j/ at the end of a word which has a short *u*.

6 **Finding Another Pattern.** On the lines below, write the words that you hear.

1. _____   3. _____

2. _____   4. _____

The /i/ in these words is called a short *i*. Write the letters that say /ij/. _____

What letters spell /j/ after a short *i*? _____

   Pattern: The letters *dge* spell /j/ at the end of a word which has a short *i*.

7 **Dictionary Skills: Alphabetizing.** Write the words below in alphabetical order on the lines provided.

chunk
rush
trunk
rung
pull
fudge
shall
full
nudge
shoe

1. _____   6. _____

2. _____   7. _____

3. _____   8. _____

4. _____   9. _____

5. _____   10. _____

8 **Writing Sentences.** On the lines below, write the sentences that you hear.

1. _____

2. _____

3. _____

4. _____

5. _____

6. _____

7. _____

8. _____

9. _____

10. _____

Review of Unit 2

The Short *u*

1 **Word Building.** Add one of the word families below to each of the letters to make a word. Do not make the same word twice.

ut	un	ud	uss
um	ub	ug	uff
up	us	uck	ull
ush	unk	ung	udge

1. b _____

2. b _____

3. c _____

4. c _____

5. d _____

6. f _____

7. g _____

8. h _____

9. h _____

10. j _____

11. l _____

12. l _____

13. m _____

14. n _____

15. p _____

16. r _____

17. r _____

18. bl _____

19. sh _____

20. st _____

21. tr _____

2 **Alphabetizing.** Alphabetize the following list of action words and write them on the lines below.

rub
judge
drum
jump
rush
dunk
scuff
rip
ship
bud

1. _____

2. _____

3. _____

4. _____

5. _____

6. _____

7. _____

8. _____

9. _____

10. _____

3 **The Ending -*ed*.** Fill in the blanks in Doubling Pattern 1 below.

Double the final consonant before adding an ending if the word has _____ syllable,

_____ vowel, and _____ final consonant, and the ending begins with a

_____.

Add -*ed* to the action words in Exercise 2, and write the new words on the
lines below. Double the final consonant when necessary.

1. _____   6. _____

2. _____   7. _____

3. _____   8. _____

4. _____   9. _____

5. _____   10. _____

4 **Creating Sentences.** Choose five of the words in Exercise 3 and use
each one in a sentence. Write the sentences on the lines below.

1. _____

   _____

2. _____

   _____

3. _____

   _____

4. _____

   _____

5. _____

   _____

5 **Finding Words in the Dictionary.** Find the words below in your dictionary. Use the two words at the top of each dictionary page to help you. On the line following each word, write the number of the page on which you find the word.

1. begun _____   6. must _____

2. cut _____   7. number _____

3. hut _____   8. nut _____

4. just _____   9. tuck _____

5. luck _____   10. under _____

6 **One-One-One Words.** Put an **X** beside each word below which has one syllable, one vowel, and ends in one consonant.

1. thus _____   5. shut _____   9. rung _____

2. gum _____   6. must _____   10. shun _____

3. begun _____   7. junk _____   11. fudge _____

4. dull _____   8. sum _____   12. thud _____

7 **The Possessive Apostrophe.** Rewrite the phrases below using an *'s* to show possession.

1. the luck of Jim _____

2. the bench of the judge _____

3. the shoe of the usher _____

4. the antlers of the buck _____

5. the bill of the duck _____

8 **Hearing Syllables.** Read the words below out loud. In the blank beside each word, write the number of syllables in the word.

1. cutting _____
2. drug _____
3. buffalo _____
4. upset _____

5. chunk _____
6. study _____
7. ugly _____
8. snuggle _____

9. struck _____
10. muffin _____
11. thundering _____
12. hunger _____

9 **Creating More Sentences.** Write three sentences. Include the words below in your sentences. You can use any form of each word.

blush   fuss   bunch   judge   lung   sing

1. _____

_____

2. _____

_____

3. _____

_____

10 **Patterns with Meaning.** Read the following sentences.

1. The *swimmer* cut his leg.
2. The *juggler* dropped the ball.
3. This *zipper* sticks.
4. My *mixer* broke.

The ending -*er* in the underlined words means _____

_____

Read these sentences.

Unhitch the horse.
He *unties* the boy's shoe.
He tried to *undo* the damage.

The prefix *un-* in the underlined words means _____

11 **Four Patterns at the End of Words.** On the lines below, write the words that you hear.

1. _____   7. _____

2. _____   8. _____

3. _____   9. _____

4. _____   10. _____

5. _____   11. _____

6. _____   12. _____

Look at the endings of the words which you have written. Now predict the endings of other words which follow the same pattern by filling in the blanks in the following sentences.

1. The letters _____ are usually used to spell the sound /k/ at the end of a one-syllable word.

2. When one-syllable words end in /f/, /l/, or /s/ the final sound is usually spelled _____, _____, or _____.

3. Use the letters _____ at the end of a word which has a short *u* and ends with the sound /j/.

4. Use the letters _____ after a consonant to spell the sound /əl/.

12 **Writing Sentences.** On the lines below, write the sentences that you hear.

1. _____
2. _____
3. _____
4. _____
5. _____
6. _____
7. _____
8. _____

13 **Crossword Puzzle.** Use the clues below to complete the crossword puzzle with words from Unit 2.

Across
1. The pitcher ____ out the batter.
3. It goes with lightning.
6. To make untidy or messy
7. Food for a squirrel
9. What tires are made of

Down
1. Quick; swift; without warning
2. He shows you to your seat.
4. One, two, or three, for instance
5. This forms on iron.
8. What you take a bath in

Lesson 12

The Word Families *et*, *en*, and *eg*

Sight Words		
car	milk	egg
stop	lettuce	listen

Word Families

et

1 **Listening**

Listen to the sound *et* makes in these words.

met	settle	carpet	basket
set	kettle	market	basketball
bet	forget	ticket	
better			

en

Listen to the sound *en* makes in these words.

hen	men	chicken	seventy
enter	women	children	sudden
center	Carmen	citizen	twenty
pencil	Ellen	driven	

eg

Listen to the sound *eg* makes in these words.

beg	leg
begged	peg
begging	

2 **Writing Words.** On the lines below, write the words that you hear.

1. _____   6. _____   11. _____

2. _____   7. _____   12. _____

3. _____   8. _____   13. _____

4. _____   9. _____   14. _____

5. _____   10. _____   15. _____

3 **Word Building.** Fill in the missing letters.

t__o   m__ __   __wo   __ __n

on__   l__ __   __ne   __ __g

thr__ __   tick__ __s   __ __ __ee   ti__kets

o__e   chic__ __ __   __ __e   ch__ __ __ __n

4 **Spelling Numbers.** Look at the words for the numbers below.

20	twenty	70	seventy
22	twenty-two	71	seventy-one
26	twenty-six	73	seventy-three

Notice the mark (-) that is used to join the words *twenty* and *two*. It is called a *hyphen*.

Pattern: A hyphen (-) is used for spelling numbers between 21 and 99 if the numbers do not end with 0 (30, 40, 50, 60, 70, 80, 90).

Write the word for each number below in the space which follows the number. Be sure to use a hyphen.

27 _____   72 _____   24 _____

77 _____   28 _____   75 _____

29 _____   76 _____   21 _____

5 **Hearing Differences: The Ending -*ing* or the Ending -*en*.** As you learned in Lesson 5, -*ing* can be added to action words. Some action words also have a form that ends with -*en*. These two endings often sound very much alike. Study the examples below.

Examples: falling   fallen

Listen carefully to the words your teacher pronounces, and write the ending you hear in the blank at the end of each word.

1. giv_____   4. driv_____   7. rott_____

2. giv_____   5. rott_____   8. tak_____

3. tak_____   6. driv_____   9. writt_____

6 **Dictionary Skills: Alphabetizing.** On the lines below, alphabetize
the words you wrote in Exercise 5.

1. _____   4. _____   7. _____

2. _____   5. _____   8. _____

3. _____   6. _____   9. _____

7 **Writing Sentences.** On the lines below, write the sentences that you hear.

1. _____

2. _____

3. _____

4. _____

5. _____

6. _____

7. _____

8. _____

9. _____

10. _____

Lesson 13

The Word Family *ed*

Sight Words		
did	before	until
not	after	because

Word Family

ed

① Listening

Listen to the sounds *ed* makes in these words.

red	Ted	fitted
shed	Fred	hundred
wedding	Ned's	wanted
medicine	gas pedal	United States

② Writing Words. On the lines below, write the words that you hear.

1. _____   4. _____   7. _____

2. _____   5. _____   8. _____

3. _____   6. _____   9. _____

③ Dictionary Skills: Words That Have an *-ed* Ending

1. Look up *fitted* in the dictionary. Is *fitted* listed in your dictionary? _____

2. Now look up the word *fit*. Is *fitted* listed after the word *fit*? _____

Some dictionaries will not list *fitted* at all. Many words that have *-ed* added to them are not listed in the dictionary.

4 **The Ending -ed.** The ending -ed is added to some words to show past time.

Present: I want to go fishing now.
Past: I wanted to go fishing yesterday.

Pattern: If you have a word which has one syllable, one vowel, and ends in one consonant, double the final consonant before adding -ed. Do not double the final consonant if the word ends in more than one consonant or in a vowel. Do not double w or x.

Make the sentences below show past time by adding -ed to the action words. Double the final consonant when necessary.

1. Ned nets fish for her.

   Ned _____ fish for her.

2. When Fred laughs, he closes his eyes.

   When Fred _____, he _____ his eyes.

3. Ed wants to see the baskets you fix.

   Ed _____ to see the baskets you _____.

4. When they finish a book, they discuss the ending.

   When they _____ a book, they _____ the ending.

5. Ellen dusts under the bed but skips the kitchen.

   Ellen _____ under the bed but _____ the kitchen.

5 **Hearing Syllables.** Write the words that you wrote in Exercise 4 on the longer lines below. On the short lines, write the number of syllables you hear in each word. Put a star (*) in front of words that have an extra syllable because -ed was added. The first one has been done to get you started.

*1. _netted_ _2_   4. _____ ____   7. _____ ____

2. _____ ____   5. _____ ____   8. _____ ____

3. _____ ____   6. _____ ____   9. _____ ____

6 **Finding a Pattern.** Write the words that you hear. Put a star (*) in front of the words in which the *-ed* ending makes an extra syllable.

1. _____   6. _____   11. _____

2. _____   7. _____   12. _____

3. _____   8. _____   13. _____

4. _____   9. _____   14. _____

5. _____   10. _____   15. _____

Look at the words above. Then fill in the blanks in the sentences below to discover new patterns.

1. The ending *-ed* makes another syllable when added to words ending with a /___/ sound or a /___/ sound.

2. The ending *-ed* does **not** make another syllable when added to words that do **not** end with a /___/ or /___/ sound.

3. Words that end with the sound /dəd/ probably end with the letters __ __ __.

4. Words that end with the sound /təd/ probably end with the letters __ __ __.

5. Now read aloud the words above that you did not mark with a * and listen to the sound *-ed* makes. The ending *-ed* can make the sound /d/, but it can make the sound /___/, too.

7 **More about the Ending -ed.** Words with an *-ed* ending are not all action words. They can also describe a person or a thing.

Example: The *netted* fish *flipped* its tail.

The word *netted* describes the fish.
The word *flipped* tells what action the fish did.

Add *-ed* to each word below. Use the new words to fill in the blanks in the sentences. The new word will describe the word that follows the blank in each sentence. The first one has been done to get you started.

     chip   cup   fit   stop   want

1. The __*wanted*__ man hid from the law.

2. We drove past the _____ car.

3. The bed has _____ sheets and blankets.

4. Ellen fixed the _____ cup.

5. Bill's _____ hands were filled with water.

8 **Writing Sentences.** On the lines below, write the sentences that you hear.

1. _____

2. _____

3. _____

4. _____

5. _____

6. _____

7. _____

8. _____

Lesson 14

The Word Families *ell* and *ess*

<table>
<tr><td colspan="3" align="center">**Sight Words**</td></tr>
<tr><td>care</td><td>when</td><td>boy</td></tr>
<tr><td>use</td><td>while</td><td>girl</td></tr>
</table>

Word Families
ell
ess

1 Listening

Listen to the sound *ell* makes in these words.

bell	fell	yell
bellhop	sell	yellow
hello	tell	spell
jelly	umbrella	spelling

Listen to the sound *ess* makes in these words.

less	mess	dress
lesson	press	dressing
unless	illness	address
careless	sickness	waitress

2 Writing Words. On the lines below, write the words that you hear.

1. _____   7. _____   13. _____

2. _____   8. _____   14. _____

3. _____   9. _____   15. _____

4. _____   10. _____   16. _____

5. _____   11. _____   17. _____

6. _____   12. _____   18. _____

3 **Hearing Differences.** At the end of words, *-ess* makes a different sound than *-es* does. Listen to the sound that *s* makes in these words that end with *-es*.

riches	mixes	ditches
wishes	fixes	brushes

What sound does the *s* in the *-es* ending make? _____

Now, listen to the sound *-ess* makes at the end of these words.

dress	recess	unless
useless	politeness	business

What sound does the *ss* in the *-ess* ending make? _____

As you learned in Lesson 4, if a word ends in *s*, *x*, *z*, *ch*, or *sh*, we add *-es* instead of just *-s*. The *e* in *-es* at the end of a word usually makes the schwa sound, /ə/. Listen to the schwa sound in the words your teacher reads. Write the words you hear.

1. _____   2. _____   3. _____

Now listen to the sound the *e* makes in *-ess*. Write the words you hear.

1. _____   2. _____   3. _____

If you hear the sound of a schwa and a *z* at the end of a word, how will it be

spelled? _____

If you hear the sound of a short *e* and an *s* at the end of a word, how will it be

spelled? _____

4 **A Pattern with Meaning: The Ending -less.** The letters -less can be added to the end of some words to make a new word. The ending -less means *not having*.

For example, adding -less to *use* creates the word *useless*. Look up the word *useless* in your dictionary. Write the meaning on the line below.

_____

On the lines below, write the word that is made by adding -less to each word given.

1. care _____   4. wing _____

2. limit _____   5. hit _____

3. drug _____   6. sun _____

5 **A Pattern with Meaning: The Ending -ness.** The letters -ness can be added to the end of some words to make a new word. The ending -ness indicates the quality, state, or condition of something.

For example, adding -ness to *ill* creates the word *illness*. Look up the word *illness* in your dictionary. Write the meaning on the line below.

_____

On the lines below, write the word that is made by adding -ness to each word given.

1. fit _____   4. rich _____

2. red _____   5. still _____

3. sick _____   6. thick _____

Notice that you do not add any letters or take any letters away when you add -less or -ness to a word.

6 **Writing Sentences.** On the lines below, write the sentences that you hear.

1. _____

2. _____

3. _____

4. _____

5. _____

_____

7 **Crossword Puzzle.** Use the clues below to complete the puzzle with word family and sight words from this lesson.

Across
1. The condition of being sick
5. To shout
6. Having no limit
7. Putting on clothes
8. Not ill
11. What this book is all about

Down
2. The opposite of careful
3. An ending indicating the quality, state, or condition of something
4. The opposite of buying
5. The color of the sun
9. The opposite of more
10. Put into action: ____ a pencil to fill in these answers.

Lesson 15

The Word Families *eck*, *edge*, and *ent*

Sight Words		
Sunday	Wednesday	Saturday
Monday	Thursday	pay
Tuesday	Friday	o'clock

Word Families

eck

edge

ent

1 Listening

Listen to the sound *eck* makes in these words.

deck	check	neck
peck	checkup	necktie
speck		paycheck

Listen to the sound *edge* makes in these words.

edge   hedge   ledge

Listen to the sound *ent* makes in these words.

bent	cent	absent
sent	rent	present
payment		different

2 Writing Words. On the lines below, write the words that you hear.

1. _____   5. _____   9. _____

2. _____   6. _____   10. _____

3. _____   7. _____   11. _____

4. _____   8. _____   12. _____

3 **The Endings -ed and -d.** In Lesson 13, you learned that -ed is added to some words to make them show past time. If a word ends with e, just add -d.

Example: judge + d ⟶ judged

Copy the sentences below, adding -ed or -d to the underlined words to make them show past time.

1. I check the payment to the dentist.

_____

2. I edge up to get my paycheck on Wednesday.

_____

3. I rent a clean ship; there is not a speck on the deck.

_____

4. When I enter Mr. Carmen's office, I pick up his mail.

_____

_____

5. You pledge to help on Fridays, but Saturdays present a problem for you.

_____

_____

4 **Dictionary Skills: Alphabetizing.** Alphabetize the *eck* words in Exercise 1 and write them on the lines below.

1. _____   4. _____   7. _____

2. _____   5. _____   8. _____

3. _____   6. _____

⑤ Writing Appointments. Write the day, time, and place of each appointment in the space after the abbreviation for the day. The first one has been done to get you started.

Sun.	Mon.	Tues.	Wed.	Thurs.	Fri.	Sat.
10:00 church	3:00 dentist	4:00 bank	11:00 Ted's	6:00 Ellen's	9:00 dentist	12:00 fitness center

Sun. *Sunday at ten o'clock at the church*

Mon. _____

Tues. _____

Wed. _____

Thurs. _____

Fri. _____

Sat. _____

⑥ Spelling Patterns

Part A. You know that the sound /k/ can be spelled different ways. The *c* in *cup*, the *ck* in *check*, and the *k* in *kitchen* all make the sound /k/. To help you to spell the sound the right way, remember that in words with one syllable, /k/ after a short vowel is spelled *ck*.

Write three words for each of the families studied so far that end with *ck*.

1. *ick* (Lesson 3) _____   _____   _____

2. *uck* (Lesson 9) _____   _____   _____

3. *eck* (Lesson 15) _____   _____   _____

Part B. You know the sound /j/ can be spelled different ways. The *J* in *Jim*, the *dge* in *edge*, and the *g* in *gentle* all make the sound /j/. To help you to spell the sound the right way, remember that in words with one syllable, /j/ after a short vowel is spelled *dge*.

Write three words for each of the families studied so far that end with *dge*.

1. *udge* (Lesson 11) _____   _____   _____

2. *edge* (Lesson 15) _____   _____   _____

Part C. Fill in the blanks in the sentences below to review the spelling patterns.

1. In words of _____ syllable, /k/ after a short vowel is spelled _____.

2. In words of one syllable, /__/ after a short vowel is spelled *dge*.

3. /k/ after a _____ vowel is spelled _____ in words of one syllable.

4. /j/ after a _____ vowel is spelled _____ in words of _____ syllable.

7 **Writing Sentences.** On the lines below, write the sentences that you hear.

1. _____

2. _____

3. _____

4. _____

5. _____

6. _____

7. _____

8. _____

Review of Unit 3

The Short *e*

1 **Writing Sentences.** On the lines below, write the sentences that you hear.

1. _____

2. _____

3. _____

4. _____

5. _____

6. _____

7. _____

_____

2 **Word Building.** Add one of the word families below to each of the letters to make a word. Do not make the same word twice.

et	*en*	*eg*
ed	*ell*	*ess*
eck	*edge*	*ent*

1. b_____   5. h_____   9. p_____   13. dr_____

2. b_____   6. l_____   10. r_____   14. pr_____

3. c_____   7. l_____   11. y_____   15. sh_____

4. d_____   8. m_____   12. ch_____   16. sp_____

3 **Hyphens in Numbers.** Spell out each number on the line beside it.

21 _____   72 _____   23 _____

74 _____   25 _____   76 _____

27 _____   78 _____   29 _____

4 Adding the -ed and -d Endings

Pattern: If the word has one syllable, one vowel, and one final consonant, double the final consonant before adding -ed. If the word ends with an e, just add -d.

Add -ed or -d to the words with spaces in the sentences below.

1. Ed beg_____ for the matter to be settle_____.

2. Meg stitch_____ the rip_____ seam in the dress.

3. Ted had a use_____ car that he care_____ for very much.

4. Ellen trip_____ when she enter_____ the carpet_____ room.

5. I check_____ the payment that we present_____ to Fred on Friday.

5 Reviewing the Ending -ed.
The ending -ed makes the sound /ed/ or /əd/ when added to words that end with t or d. The ending -ed also makes a separate syllable when added to words that end with t or d.

On the lines below, write the words that you hear.

1. _____   4. _____   7. _____

2. _____   5. _____   8. _____

3. _____   6. _____   9. _____

6 Reviewing the Ending -es.
The ending -es makes the sound /əz/ when added to words that end with s, x, z, ch, or sh. The ending -es also makes a separate syllable when added to words that end with s, x, z, ch, or sh.

On the lines below, write the words that you hear.

1. _____   6. _____   11. _____

2. _____   7. _____   12. _____

3. _____   8. _____   13. _____

4. _____   9. _____   14. _____

5. _____   10. _____   15. _____

7 Reviewing the Endings -s, -es, and -ess

The ending -s is added to words to show more than one. It is also added to action words to show action by a he, a she, or an it. The ending -s makes the sound /s/ or /z/.

The ending -es is added to words that end with s, x, z, ch, or sh to show more than one. It is also added to action words that end with s, x, z, ch, or sh to show action by a he, a she, or an it. The ending -es makes the sound /əz/ and makes a separate syllable.

The ending -ess makes the sound /es/ at the end of a word. Many words are built with -ness or -less at the end.

On the lines below, write the words that you hear.

1. _____   6. _____   11. _____

2. _____   7. _____   12. _____

3. _____   8. _____   13. _____

4. _____   9. _____   14. _____

5. _____   10. _____   15. _____

8 One-Syllable Words Ending with /k/ and /j/

Pattern: In words with one syllable, /k/ after a short vowel is spelled *ck*.

Pattern: In words with one syllable, /j/ after a short vowel is spelled *dge*.

On the lines below, write the sentences that you hear.

1. _____

2. _____

3. _____

4. _____

5. _____

6. _____

9 **Abbreviations for the Days of the Week.** Write the days of the week in order on the lines at the left. Start with Sunday. Write their abbreviations on the lines at the right. Use a dictionary if necessary.

Day of the Week   **Abbreviation**

1. _____   _____

2. _____   _____

3. _____   _____

4. _____   _____

5. _____   _____

6. _____   _____

7. _____   _____

10 **Creating Sentences.** Write a paragraph of at least three sentences about this picture.

_____

_____

_____

_____

_____

Lesson 16

The Word Families *ot*, *on*, *ong*, and *op*

Sight Words				
Mr.	Miss	male	married	separated
Mrs.	Ms.	female	single	divorced

Word Families

ot

1 Listening

Listen to the sound *ot* makes in these words.

got	knot	forgot
hot	shot	bottle
lot	spot	cotton

on

Listen to the sound *on* makes in these words.

on	bonnet	pond
onto	honest	fond
upon	crayon	donkey

ong

Listen to the sound *ong* makes in these words.

song	belong
long	strong
along	wrong

op

Listen to the sound *op* makes in these words.

hop	chop	bellhop
mop	stop	copper
top	shopping	operator

2 Writing Words. On the lines below, write the words that you hear.

1. _____   6. _____

2. _____   7. _____

3. _____   8. _____

4. _____   9. _____

5. _____   10. _____

3 Word Building. Add one of the endings below to each of the following words to make a new form of the word. Write the new word on the line provided. Double the final consonant when necessary.

-ed   -er   -ing

1. hop _____   6. drop _____

2. top _____   7. stop _____

3. shop _____   8. mop _____

4. spot _____   9. pop _____

5. chop _____   10. prop _____

4 A Pattern with Meaning: non-. Add non- to the beginning of each of these words. Write the new word on the lines provided.

1. stop _____   3. metal _____

2. sense _____   4. skid _____

What do you think non- means?

_____

Look up non- in your dictionary. Write the definition below.

_____

5 **Contractions with *Not*.** When we put two words together and leave out one or more letters, we have a contraction. The word *not* is often used in a contraction. Study the example below.

Example: *is not* becomes *isn't*

Notice that we put an apostrophe (') in place of the *o* which we left out. Now write these words as contractions.

1. are not   _____   3. would not _____

2. should not _____   4. could not _____

Write the contraction for *will not* by changing the word *will*. _____

Now write three sentences below. Use a contraction in each one.

1. _____

2. _____

3. _____

6 **Dictionary Skills.** As you learned in Lesson 9, certain symbols in the dictionary show us how to pronounce a word. Look up the words *not* and *knot*. Write the pronunciation for each word on the lines provided.

1. not _____   2. knot _____

Notice that these two words are pronounced the same way.

In most dictionaries the symbol used to show the pronunciation of these words is ⌣. This symbol is used to indicate a short vowel.

7 ***Not* or *Knot*.** Write a sentence using the word *not*. Then write a sentence using the word *knot*.

1. not: _____

2. knot: _____

8 **A Lot.** *A lot* is two words. This expression is frequently misspelled as one word. *Lot* is used to mean a great many. Sometimes we say *lots*.

Examples: I have a lot of food.
I have lots of food.

Use the expression *a lot* in a sentence of your own.

a lot: _____

9 **Words for Filling out Forms.** Fill out this section of a form.

Name: _____
         Last   First   Middle

Date: _____   Social Security Number: _____

Sex: _____   Marital Status: _____

10 **Writing Sentences.** On the lines below, write the sentences that you hear.

1. _____

2. _____

3. _____

4. _____

5. _____

6. _____

7. _____

8. _____

Lesson 17

The Word Families *ob*, *ock*, and *ox*

Sight Words			
street	St.	drive	Dr.
avenue	Ave.	apartment	Apt.
road	Rd.		

Word Families

ob

ock

ox

① Listening

Listen to the sound *ob* makes in these words.

Bob	hobby
job	robin
rob	problem

Listen to the sound *ock* makes in these words.

lock	block	o'clock
rock	clock	pocket
sock	flock	stockings

Listen to the sound *ox* makes in these words.

ox	box	fox

② Writing Words. On the lines below, write the words that you hear.

1. _____   6. _____

2. _____   7. _____

3. _____   8. _____

4. _____   9. _____

5. _____   10. _____

3 **Hearing Syllables.** Write the number of syllables in each word you hear.

1. _____   3. _____   5. _____

2. _____   4. _____   6. _____

4 **Spelling Words with Many Syllables.** On the lines below, write the words that you hear.

1. _____   5. _____

2. _____   6. _____

3. _____   7. _____

4. _____   8. _____

5 **The Word Families *ocks* and *ox*.** Rewrite each of these words, adding *-s* to make them plural. Then say each of the plural words aloud.

1. lock _____   4. block _____

2. sock _____   5. clock _____

3. knock _____   6. flock _____

Now say each of these words aloud: locks   box

What do you notice about the pronunciation of the ends of these words?

_____

What do you notice about the spelling of the ends of these words?

_____

> **Pattern:** The word families *ocks* and *ox* are pronounced the same way. *Ocks* is used as the plural of words ending in *ock*. *Ox* is found in a few singular nouns.

6 **More Contractions.** Write the contractions for the following words.

1. should not _____   2. would not _____

Words other than *not* can also be used in contractions. For example, the contraction for *he is* is *he's*. The apostrophe (') takes the place of the *i* in *is*.

Figure out what letter or letters are left out when you put together the pairs of words below. Write each contraction, putting an apostrophe where you leave out the letters.

1. I am	_____	7. I shall	_____	13. he would	_____
2. she is	_____	8. you will	_____	14. she has	_____
3. we are	_____	9. he will	_____	15. we have	_____
4. you are	_____	10. she will	_____	16. you have	_____
5. they are	_____	11. they will	_____	17. can not	_____
6. let us	_____	12. you would	_____	18. do not	_____

7 **Personal Word List for Filling out Forms.** Fill in the information below to develop your own word list to use when you fill out forms.

Your full name _____

Your maiden name _____ Your middle initial _____

Your street address _____

Your city _____ Your county _____

Your state _____ Your zip code _____

Your telephone number (include area code) _____

Your social security number _____ Your sex _____

Your marital status _____ Your citizenship _____

8 **Filling out Forms.** Complete this section of an employment application form.

Application for Employment

Date _____ Social Security Number _____

Name _____
<u>Last</u>   <u>First</u>   <u>Middle</u>

Address _____
<u>Street</u>   <u>Apt.</u>

_____
City   County   State   Zip Code

Phone no. _____ U.S. citizen? _____ yes _____ no
(area code)

---

9 **Writing Sentences.** On the lines below, write the sentences that you hear.

1. _____

2. _____

3. _____

4. _____

5. _____

_____

Lesson 18

The Word Families *od* and *odge*

Sight Words		
elementary school	part-time	company, Co.
high school	full-time	diploma
grade		

Word Families

od

1 Listening

Listen to the sound *od* makes in these words.

rod	fodder
God	
nod	

odge

Listen to the sound *odge* makes in these words.

dodge
lodge
hodge-podge

2 Writing Words. On the lines below, write the words that you hear.

1. _____
2. _____
3. _____

4. _____
5. _____
6. _____

3 Word Building. Write three words which rhyme with *rod*. Do not use words which appear in Exercise 1. Check your dictionary to see if your words are there.

1. _____   2. _____   3. _____

4 **More Word Building.** Add *-odge*, *-edge*, *-udge*, or *-idge* to each of the consonants below to make a word. Do not make the same word twice.

1. b_____   6. l_____

2. d_____   7. n_____

3. f_____   8. r_____

4. h_____   9. br_____

5. j_____   10. sm_____

5 **Rediscovering a Pattern**

Pattern: Use the letters _____ to spell the /j/ sound at the end of a one-syllable word which has a short vowel.

Make a word with *-odge*, *-edge*, *-udge*, or *-idge* to complete each of these sentences. Write the word in the blank.

1. The kids were playing _____ ball.

2. I ate some peanut butter _____.

3. Rod had to trim the _____ in his yard.

4. The two islands are joined by a _____.

5. The _____ sentenced him to four years in prison.

6 **Dictionary Skills: Alphabetizing.** Write the following words in alphabetical order on the lines provided.

employer   1. _____   6. _____
supervisor
occupation   2. _____   7. _____
business
performed   3. _____   8. _____
telephone
single   4. _____   9. _____
education
address   5. _____   10. _____
signature

7 **Writing Sentences.** On the lines below, write the sentences that you hear.

1. _____

2. _____

3. _____

4. _____

5. _____

6. _____

7. _____

8. _____

8 **Personal Word List for Filling out Forms.** Fill in the information below to continue your own word list to use when you fill out forms.

Your date of birth _____ Your place of birth _____

Your occupation _____ Are you a veteran? _____

Name and address of your most recent employer _____

_____

Type of business _____ Dates employed _____

Work performed _____

Name and title of your supervisor _____

Name and address of the last school you attended _____

_____

Were you ever convicted of a felony? _____ If yes, give details _____

_____

9 **Filling out Forms.** Imagine that you are divorced and have a three-year-old son. He has fallen and broken his leg. The accident occurred on January 5 of this year. Complete the form below to file a claim with your health insurance plan.

Medical Claim Form

Patient Information

Patient's Name (Last, First, Middle)	Relationship to Member	Sex	Date of Birth
		___ M ___ F	

Was accident or illness due to employment: ___ Yes ___ No

If child, does member have responsibility for patient's bill? ___ Yes ___ No

Member Information

Member's Name (Last, First, Middle)	Social Security No.	Sex	Date of Birth
		___ M ___ F	

Member's Address (Street, City, State, Zip)

Home Phone	Work Phone	Marital Status	Is Spouse Employed?
			___ Yes ___ No

Claim Information

Description of accident or illness

	Date of accident or illness

Patient's signature _____
(Guardian, if minor)

Member's signature _____

Review of Unit 4

The Short *o*

1 Word Building: Contractions

Part A. Complete each sentence by writing a contraction of the words under the blank.

1. _____ sing that song for Bob.
   (Let us)

2. _____ getting married on Saturday.
   (I am)

3. The girl _____ listen to her sister.
   (would not)

4. She _____ be having the operation.
   (will not)

5. _____ going to the elementary school.
   (We are)

Part B. Write the two words that make up each contraction below.

1. she'd _____   4. wouldn't _____

2. you're _____   5. they're _____

3. weren't _____   6. he's _____

2 Root Words. Write the root word in each word below.

1. locker _____   6. nonskid _____

2. fondness _____   7. unlock _____

3. noncombat _____   8. nonrigid _____

4. unknot _____   9. robber _____

5. jobless _____   10. nonstop _____

3 **Writing Words Ending with x or cks.** On the lines below write the words that your teacher dictates. Then write the root word beside each word you wrote. Some words will not change.

1. _____   _____   4. _____   _____

2. _____   _____   5. _____   _____

3. _____   _____   6. _____   _____

4 **Rediscovering a Pattern**

Pattern: Use the letters _____ to spell the /j/ sound at the end of a one-syllable word which has a short vowel.

Write the sentences you hear.

1. _____

2. _____

3. _____

4. _____

5 **Short Vowels**

1. Write the symbol used to mark a short vowel. _____

2. Write three words which have a short *u* sound.

_____   _____   _____

3. Write three words which have a short *i* sound.

_____   _____   _____

4. Write three words which have a short *e* sound.

_____   _____   _____

5. Write three words which have a short *o* sound.

_____   _____   _____

6 **Hearing Syllables.** Write each word that you hear one syllable at a time. Then write the whole word on the line provided. The first one has been done to get you started.

First Syllable	Second Syllable	Whole Word
1. *prob*	*lem*	*problem*
2.		
3.		
4.		
5.		
6.		
7.		
8.		
9.		
10.		
11.		
12.		

7 **Dictionary Skills: Pronunciation.** Look up each word in the dictionary. Then write the pronunciation on the line provided.

1. block _____

2. box _____

3. chop _____

4. copper _____

5. dodge _____

6. hobby _____

7. single _____

8. wrong _____

8 **Filling out a Form.** Fill in the information requested on the form below. Use words from your personal word lists in Lessons 17 and 18.

Application for Employment

Name _____ Date _____

Address _____

City _____ State _____ Zip _____ U.S. citizen? _____

Telephone (____) _____ Social Security No. _____

Position applied for: _____ Date available: _____

Interested in: ____ Full time? ____ Part time? Are you a veteran? _____

Education:

	Name of school	Address of school	Dates From	To	Did You Graduate?	Course or Degree
High School						
College or University						
Business or Trade School						

Most Recent Employment:

Name of Company _____ Telephone _____

Address of Company _____

Type of Business _____ Dates Employed _____

Work Performed _____

Name and Title of Supervisor _____

Salary _____ Reason for Leaving _____

Were you ever convicted of a felony? ____ If yes, give details _____

_____

9 **Creating Sentences.** Write a paragraph of at least three sentences about this picture.

_____

_____

_____

_____

_____

_____

_____

_____

_____

_____

_____

_____

10 **Crossword Puzzle.** Use the clues below to complete the puzzle with words from this unit.

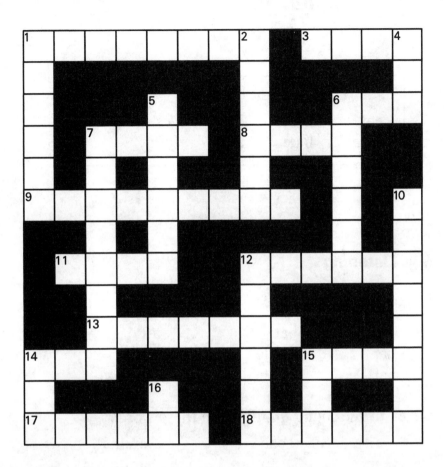

Across

1. They carry suitcases.
3. Not short: a ___ time ago
6. Opposite of cold
7. ___, look, and listen.
8. Upon; on top of
9. Women wear these on their feet and legs.
11. A stain or blot
12. A container for liquids
13. Bobbing the head in agreement
14. To run slowly
15. A small piece of land; a plan
17. Be a member of: I ___ to the club.
18. Teeter-___ (a seesaw)

Down

1. Children build things with these.
2. Not weak
4. Received: I ___ a present.
5. The part of a garment to put things in
6. Truthful; not lying, cheating, or stealing
7. A group of stores is a ___ center.
10. She says, "Number, please."
12. A hat for Easter
14. Work: A ___ well done
15. Used for cooking or to put a plant in
16. Opposite of off

Lesson 19

The Word Families *at*, *an*, *ab*, and *as*

```
┌─────────────────────────────────────────────────────┐
│                    Sight Words                       │
│   eat      ate      like      yesterday              │
│   meat     hate     date      today                  │
└─────────────────────────────────────────────────────┘
```

Word Families

① Listening

at

Listen to the sound *at* makes in these words.

at	bat	attic	battery
cat	battle	scatter	matter
hat	cattle	Saturday	that's

an

Listen to the sound *an* makes in these words.

an	can	animal
man	cannot	janitor
Dan	Canada	January

ab

Listen to the sound *ab* makes in these words.

cab	grab	cabbage
cabin	rabbit	tablet
cabinet	absent	

as

Listen to the sounds *as* makes in these words.

as	gas	master
has	gas pedal	pasture
hasn't	gas tank	

② Hearing Sounds. The *s* in the family *as* makes two different sounds.

Listen to the words *as*, *has*, and *hasn't*. What sound does the *s* make? _____

What sound does the *s* make in *gas*, *master*, and *pasture*? _____

3 **Writing Words.** On the lines below, write the words that you hear.

1. _____   6. _____   11. _____

2. _____   7. _____   12. _____

3. _____   8. _____   13. _____

4. _____   9. _____   14. _____

5. _____   10. _____   15. _____

4 **Creating Sentences.** Write three sentences that use some of the words from Exercise 1. Try to use several in each sentence.

1. _____

_____

2. _____

_____

3. _____

_____

5 **Dictionary Skills: Alphabetizing.** Below are pairs of words that are at the top of pages in an imaginary dictionary. For each pair, write three words from the word families *at*, *an*, *ab*, or *as* that would be on the same page.

abet——attack   cab——cave   rabbi——rattle   T——tattered

_____   _____   _____   _____

_____   _____   _____   _____

_____   _____   _____   _____

6 **Showing Past Time.** Change the sentences below to make them show past time. Start each sentence you write with the word *Yesterday*. In some cases, you will add *-ed* to the action words to show past time. In other cases, the action words will change in other ways.

Example: The janitor grabs the mop and goes.
Yesterday the janitor grabbed the mop and went.

1. Dan has that car fixed.

_____

2. That woman tans in the sun.

_____

3. Nat and Dan run a mile-long race.

_____

4. Fran grabs at the hat but misses.

_____

5. That man plans to visit Canada.

_____

6. They eat a sandwich and pickles for lunch.

_____

7. Stan takes a cab that rattles like thunder.

_____

8. Pat masters all the problems in the lesson.

_____

_____

7 **Building Words.** Fill in the missing letters in the silly story below. The words with letters missing are all from Exercise 1.

Dan and his brother Stan work as j_ _itors at a pet shop in Toronto, C_ _ada. They are both good _t their jobs, but D_ _ is a better worker. Stan is sometimes _bsent when he is not sick, but _ _n h_ _n't missed a day without something being the m_ _ter. He _as as much energy as a b_ttery. Stan is slow _t his work, but he does get it done.

One day D_ _ saw Stan taking a c_ _ nap in the _ _tic. He didn't know what to do. Then _an went down into the shop and got a large c_ _bage. He went back up to the a_ _ic and sc_ _tered bits of the _ _bbage on Stan. After that he got a r_ _bit from a pen and set the _ _ imal free near Stan. He planned to have the _ _bbit wake Stan up, but it ate Stan's favorite h_ _ instead.

Now Stan doesn't nap in the _ _tic anymore.

8 **Writing Sentences.** On the lines below, write the sentences that you hear.

1. _____
2. _____
3. _____
4. _____
5. _____
6. _____
7. _____
8. _____

Lesson 20

The Word Families *ad*, *am*, *ag*, and *ap*

Sight Words				
red	yellow	blue	white	black
orange	green	purple	gray	brown

Word Families

① Listening

ad

Listen to the sound *ad* makes in these words.

bad	sad	radish
had	glad	saddle
lad	admit	shadow
mad	ladder	want ads

am

Listen to the sound *am* makes in these words.

Pam	ham	exam
Sam	hammer	examination
Sam's	hamburger	program
damage	family	grammar

ag

Listen to the sound *ag* makes in these words.

bag	rag	flag
tag	drag	wagon

ap

Listen to the sound *ap* makes in these words.

lap	slap	apple
map	snap	application
nap	happy	napkin
clap	happen	road map

2 **The Endings -*ing* and -*ed*.** Fill in each blank with the correct form of the word in parentheses. You will need to add either -*ed* or -*ing* to each word.

Remember, if you have a word which has one syllable, one vowel, and ends in one consonant, double the last consonant before adding -*ed* or -*ing*.

1. (nap)   Jill is still _____.

2. (clap)   We _____ as Brad finished the race.

3. (pad)   The _____ crib was blue and yellow.

4. (saddle)   Carmen _____ the horse while I waited.

5. (bag)   Pam was _____ the lettuce and white radishes.

6. (slap)   Ed _____ a price tag on the red wagon.

7. (grab)   Alan _____ a bite to eat on his way to class.

8. (damage)   The _____ gas tank needed to be replaced.

3 **Dictionary Skills.** On the lines below, write all the three-letter words which end in -*ad*. Use the dictionary if you need to. The first one has been done to get you started.

1. _bad_   4. _____   7. _____   10. _____

2. _____   5. _____   8. _____   11. _____

3. _____   6. _____   9. _____   12. _____

How does the dictionary show the sound of *a* in *bad*? _____

Words that rhyme with *bad* will all show the same sound for *a*. Did you find a word that

does not rhyme with *bad*? _____ If you did, write it on this line. _____

4 **Writing Sentences.** On the lines below, write the sentences that you hear.

1. _____

2. _____

3. _____

4. _____

5. _____

6. _____

7. _____

8. _____

9. _____

10. _____

_____

5 **Creating Sentences.** On the lines below, describe a room you like to be in. Use as many of the color sight words in this lesson as you can.

_____

_____

_____

_____

_____

6 **Crossword Puzzle.** Use the clues below to complete the crossword with the word family and sight words from this lesson.

Across

1. ___, crackle, and pop
3. A tool to use with nails
6. A cushion; sheets of paper glued together
7. A taxi
9. Red and yellow mixed together make this.
10. A test
13. The color of the sun
15. Not happy
16. The color of a stop light
17. The rules for using words in a language

Down

1. What is cast when the sun shines
2. Short for Pamela
3. Occur
4. Angry
5. Used to find your way when driving (two words)
8. The opposite of sad
11. It has rungs for climbing.
12. The color of the sky
14. What dogs' tails do
15. Short for Samuel

Lesson 21

The Word Families *ax*, *ack*, *ask*, and *ang*

Sight Words			
in	into	through	beside
on	over	between	behind

Word Families

① Listening

ax

Listen to the sound *ax* makes in these words.

ax	lax
tax	relax

ack

Listen to the sound *ack* makes in these words.

pack	back	black	shack
rack	backwards	crack	snack
sack	lack	cracker	track

ask

Listen to the sound *ask* makes in these words.

ask	mask
task	masking tape

ang

Listen to the sound *ang* makes in these words.

hang	sang
rang	angry
	language

2 **Distinguishing Sounds.** When -*s* is added to words that end with the *ack* family, they will sound like words in the *ax* family.

Ax sounds like *acks*.
Ax and *acks* do not sound like *ask*.

Part A. Listen to each pair of words as your teacher reads them. Circle the number if the words sound the same.

1. tax——task
2. tacks——tax
3. task——tacks

4. lax——lacks
5. ax——ask
6. tags——tasks

Part B. Listen to each pair of words as your teacher reads them. Circle the number if the words contain syllables with the same sound.

1. relax——lax
2. mask——maximum
3. Ajax——Jack's

4. task——attacks
5. attacks——tax
6. backs——basket

Part C. Now look at the numbers you circled in Part B. Underline the letters that make the same sounds in those pairs.

3 **Writing Sentences.** On the lines below, write the sentences that you hear.

1. _____
2. _____
3. _____
4. _____
5. _____
6. _____
7. _____
8. _____

4 **Using the Sight Words.** Select one of the sight words listed below to fill in each blank in the sentences below. Words can be used more than once.

in	into	through	beside
on	over	between	behind

1. The man and woman are _____ the living room.

2. The pillow is _____ the woman and the man _____ the sofa.

3. The man seems to be sinking _____ the sofa.

4. The afghan is draped _____ the back of the sofa.

5. The lamp is _____ the chair and sofa.

6. The lamp is _____ the table _____ the sofa.

7. The window is _____ the table.

8. You can see a tree _____ the window.

9. The chair is _____ the table.

10. The cat is napping _____ the chair.

5 **Dictionary Skills: Alphabetizing.** The list below contains three words that are not in the correct alphabetical order. Circle the numbers of the words that are out of alphabetical order.

1. angry	7. crack	13. mask	19. sack
2. ask	8. cracker	14. masking	20. shack
3. ax	9. hang	15. pack	21. snacks
4. black	10. lack	16. rang	22. sang
5. back	11. language	17. relax	23. task
6. backwards	12. lax	18. rack	24. tax

6 **Word Building.** Words made by combining two words are called *compound words*. Make compound words by combining the sets of words below. Write the compound words on the lines provided. The first one has been done to get you started.

1. tax + payer _taxpayer_   6. scatter + brain _____

2. back + pack _____   7. master + mind _____

3. black + board _____   8. cracker + jack _____

4. man + made _____   9. slap + stick _____

5. basket + ball _____   10. apple + sauce _____

Choose four of the compound words above. Use each of them in a sentence.

1. _____

_____

2. _____

_____

3. _____

_____

4. _____

_____

Lesson 22

The Word Families *ass*, *ash*, *atch*, and *ath*

<table>
<tr><td colspan="3">Sight Words</td></tr>
<tr><td>thirty</td><td>fifty</td><td>eighty</td></tr>
<tr><td>forty</td><td>sixty</td><td>ninety</td></tr>
</table>

Word Families

1 **Listening**

ass

Listen to the sound *ass* makes in these words.

bass	brass	class
mass	glass	classified
pass	grass	

ash

Listen to the sound *ash* makes in these words.

| ash | dash | cash |
| bash | mash | cashier |

atch

Listen to the sound *atch* makes in these words.

| catch | hatch | patch |
| match | latch | scratch |

ath

Listen to the sound *ath* makes in these words.

| bath | path | math |

2 **Writing Words.** On the lines below, write the words that you hear.

1. _____   5. _____   9. _____   13. _____

2. _____   6. _____   10. _____   14. _____

3. _____   7. _____   11. _____   15. _____

4. _____   8. _____   12. _____   16. _____

3 **Word Building.** Fill in the missing letters in the story below. The words with letters missing are all from Exercise 1.

Ben was trying to pa__ __ another car when his car hit a p__ __ch of g__ __ __ __s and slid into the ditch. Ben hit his hand on the d__sh, but it wasn't scr__ __ __hed. He was lucky his hand hadn't gone through the g__ __s__. He tried to get out of the car, but the __atc__ stuck. He finally got out through the h__t__h. He tried to c__t__ __ a ride to town, but no other cars __ __ssed him. So he walked the whole way back.

4 **The Endings -s and -es.** Words that end with s, x, z, ch or sh have -es added to them to show there is more than one thing. Action words that end with s, x, z, ch or sh will have -es added to them to show that a he, a she, or an it is doing the action.

Add -s or -es as needed in the spaces in the sentences below. Remember that -es makes another syllable when it is added to a word.

1. I wish I had three wish_____ to make.

2. Fred catch_____ bass when he fish_____.

3. Ron mash_____ apple_____ to make apple butter.

4. Ellen lost her eyeglass_____ and eighty cent_____.

5. One of the two path_____ pass_____ by the plant.

6. Try to get three patch_____ for Dan's rubber duck_____.

7. Some children don't like bath_____, but Ed seem_____ to think they are fun.

8. Sam lit the fire with match_____ and then watched until only ash_____ were left.

5 **Using the Sight Words.** You can write large numbers with the sight words in this lesson. Remember to use a hyphen (-) with numbers between 21 and 99 unless they end in zero. Write the numbers below on the lines provided. The first one has been done to get you started.

347 _____three hundred forty-seven_____

93 _____

234 _____

55 _____

890 _____

46 _____

82 _____

456 _____

37 _____

68 _____

6 **Writing Sentences.** On the lines below, write the sentences that you hear.

1. _____

2. _____

3. _____

4. _____

5. _____

6. _____

7. _____

8. _____

_____

7 **Crossword Puzzle.** Use the clues below to complete the crossword with words from the word families in this lesson.

Across

1. A track through the grass
3. He is ___ tall as I am.
4. Windows are made of this.
7. At a store, the person you give your money to
8. A kind of fish
9. A course where you study numbers
10. A group of students
11. Eggs do this.
12. A small cut; what to do to an itch

Down

1. What you hope to do at the end of a course
2. Something that burns turns to this.
4. It is green and you mow it.
5. What you tie around the waist of a dress
6. Used to cover a hole or rip
7. To capture, grab, or trap
8. A ___ of cookies
9. Used to start a fire
10. Money

Review of Unit 5

The Short *a*

1 **Writing Sentences.** On the lines below, write the sentences that you hear.

1. _____

2. _____

3. _____

4. _____

5. _____

6. _____

7. _____

8. _____

2 **Word Building.** Write one of the word families below in each blank to make a word. Do not make the same word twice.

at	ab	ad	ag	ax	ask	ass	atch
an	as	am	ap	ack	ang	ash	ath

1. b_____   5. l_____   9. r_____   13. sc_____

2. c_____   6. m_____   10. r_____   14. sh_____

3. h_____   7. p_____   11. br_____   15. sl_____

4. l_____   8. p_____   12. ch_____   16. scr_____

3 **The Two Sounds of s.** As you have seen, the letter *s* can have two sounds. Fill in the blanks in the sentences below to review the two sounds of *s*.

The *s* in *has* makes the /___/ sound. The *s* in *gas* makes the /___/ sound.

Two words in which *s* makes the /z/ sound are _____ and _____.

Two words in which *s* makes the /s/ sound are _____ and _____.

4 **Word Building.** Compound words can be written as one word, as two words with a hyphen between them, or as two separate words. Write the compound words built from the pairs of words below. Look them up in the dictionary first to see how they should be written.

1. yellow + jacket _____

2. green + house _____

3. white + cap _____

4. white + flag _____

5. blue + grass _____

6. red + letter _____

7. red + handed _____

8. black + ball _____

9. black + jack _____

10. gray + matter _____

5 **Distinguishing Sounds.** Listen to the words your teacher reads to you. They will contain one of two sounds after the short vowel:

1. /ks/, spelled *cks* or *x*, or
2. /sk/, spelled *sk*.

In the left column, write each word that has /ks/ in it. In the right column, write each word that has /sk/ in it.

/ks/	/sk/
_____	_____
_____	_____
_____	_____
_____	_____
_____	_____
_____	_____
_____	_____

6 **Root Words.** On the lines at the left, write the words that your teacher dictates to you. Then write the root word on the shorter lines at the right. Some pairs will be the same.

	Dictated Word	Root Word		Dictated Word	Root Word
1.	_____	_____	7.	_____	_____
2.	_____	_____	8.	_____	_____
3.	_____	_____	9.	_____	_____
4.	_____	_____	10.	_____	_____
5.	_____	_____	11.	_____	_____
6.	_____	_____	12.	_____	_____

7 **Hearing Syllables.** Write the words that you hear one syllable at a time. Then write the whole word on the line at the right.

	First Syllable	Second Syllable	Third Syllable	Whole Word
1.	_____	_____		_____
2.	_____	_____	_____	_____
3.	_____	_____	_____	_____
4.	_____	_____		_____
5.	_____	_____		_____
6.	_____	_____	_____	_____
7.	_____	_____	_____	_____

8 **Using Words.** Fill in the blanks in the story with one of the words below. Use each word only once.

animals	can	grabs	latch	shack	thirty
axes	cattle	hangs	path	shadows	through
back	eats	lack	sack	that	wagon

Brad Baxter and his family live on a farm _____ miles from town. Even in winter there is no _____ of work to do on the farm. Each morning Brad gets up early and _____ breakfast with his wife and son. Then he has to go out to feed all the _____. He trudges _____ the snow to the barn. There he _____ a big _____ of corn and feeds the hens and chickens. Then he feeds the horses and _____. After _____, he fixes the _____ on the barn door.

Meanwhile Alan, Brad's son, walks along a _____ to a _____ behind the house. He gets one of the _____ stored there so he _____ chop firewood.

Later, Brad and Alan fix the broken axle on their hay _____. As the sun _____ low in the sky, casting long _____, they finish the day's work and go _____ to the house.

Review of Book 1

The Short Vowel Word Families

Short *i* Lessons 1-6	Short *u* Lessons 7-11	Short *e* Lessons 12-15	Short *o* Lessons 16-18	Short *a* Lessons 19-22
ib	ub		ob	ab
ich				
ick	uck	eck	ock	ack
id	ud	ed	od	ad
	udge	edge	odge	
iff	uff			
ig	ug	eg		ag
ill	ull	ell		
im	um			am
in	un	en	on	an
ing	ung		ong	ang
	unk			
		ent		
ip	up		op	ap
is	us			as
ish	ush			ash
				ask
iss	uss	ess		ass
it	ut	et	ot	at
itch				atch
				ath
ive				
ix			ox	ax

1 **Hearing Word Families.** On the lines below, write the word families you hear.

1. _____ 5. _____ 9. _____ 13. _____ 17. _____ 21. _____

2. _____ 6. _____ 10. _____ 14. _____ 18. _____ 22. _____

3. _____ 7. _____ 11. _____ 15. _____ 19. _____ 23. _____

4. _____ 8. _____ 12. _____ 16. _____ 20. _____ 24. _____

2 **Reviewing the Short Vowel Families.** Look at the chart on the left to fill in the blanks in the statements below.

1. Which of the families in the chart do *not* end with a consonant? _____, _____, _____, and _____.

2. Families that end with /j/ are spelled with __ __ __ at the end.

3. Families that end with /k/ are spelled with __ __ at the end.

4. The family that ends with /v/ is spelled with __ __ at the end.

5. Families that end with a doubled consonant are spelled with __ __, __ __, and __ __ at the end.

3 **Reviewing Patterns.** Fill in the blanks in the statements below to review some of the patterns you learned in this text.

1. The endings -*s* and -*es* show that there is more than _____ of a thing.

2. The endings -*s* and -*es* added to _____ words show that a he, a she, or an it is doing the action.

3. If a word ends in *s*, *x*, *z*, *ch*, or *sh*, add _____ instead of -*s*.

4. The endings -*ed* or -*d* are added to some action words to show _____ time.

5. After the letter _____ or _____, the -*ed* ending makes a separate syllable.

6. Double the final consonant if a word has _____ syllable, _____ vowel, and _____ final consonant and the ending begins with a _____. Do not double *w* or *x*.

4 **Adding Endings.** Add the endings at the top of the columns to each word on the left.

	-s or -es	-ed or -d	-ing
1. kick			
2. rent			
3. fuss			
4. relax			
5. pit			
6. stuff			
7. stop			
8. match			
9. wish			
10. judge			
11. hop			
12. thunder			

5 **Writing Sentences.** On the lines below, write the sentences that you hear.

1. _____

2. _____

3. _____

4. _____

5. _____

6. _____
   _____

6 **Review of Patterns with Meaning.** Review the patterns with meaning below.

Un- and *non-* are added to the beginning of some words to add the meaning *not*.

The ending *-less* added to a word adds the meaning *without*.

The ending *-ness* added to a word indicates a quality, state, or condition.

The ending *-er* is added to some words to show a person.

Now write the words indicated by the definitions given.

1. not buckled   _____

2. not fiction   _____

3. without limit   _____

4. the condition of being ill   _____

5. a person who swims   _____

6. a person who does not swim   _____

7 **Review of the Schwa.** Fill in the blanks in the statements below.

1. The sound /əl/ at the end of a word is usually spelled _____.

2. The sounds /dəd/ or /təd/ at the end of a word usually mean ___ ___ was added after a *d* or *t*.

3. The sound /əz/ after *s, x, z, ch,* or *sh* is usually spelled _____.

4. The *-er* ending often makes the sound /___r/.

On the lines below, write the sentence that you hear.

_____

_____

8 **Filling out Forms.** Imagine that while at work you slipped on a wet floor, fell, cut the little finger of your left hand, and twisted your left leg. This happened on August 24 of this year. Fill out this accident report for your employer, Trickle's Fickle Pickles, who insures you under the TFP Health Plan.

TFP Health Plan Accident Report

Date _____ Social Security Number _____-_____-_____

Name _____ Date of Birth _____
     Last   First   M.I.   Mo./Day/Yr.

Current Residence _____
     Street Address   Apt. No.

_____
 City   County   State   Zip

Phone _____-_____-_____ Date of Accident _____
    (Area Code)

Brief Description of Accident (Attach additional paper if necessary.)

_____

_____

_____

_____

_____

_____

_____

_____

Signature _____

---

9 **Crossword Puzzle.** Use the clues below to help you fill in the puzzle with the sight words from this text.

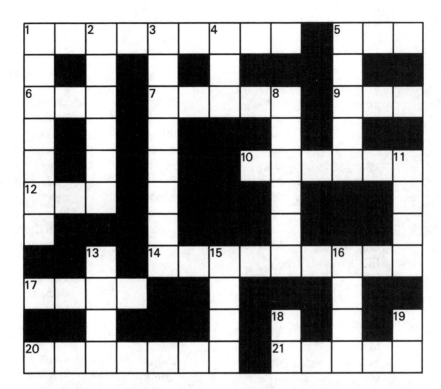

Across

1. A group of rooms to live in
5. Also
6. I am, he is, we ___
7. He worked ___ he finished the job.
9. The first color in the rainbow
10. A road in a town or city
12. A he, a ___, or an it
14. The day before today
17. What we see with
20. A green, leafy vegetable
21. Here, ___, and everywhere

Down

1. Opposed to: It is ___ the law to park there.
2. A wide street
3. The day after Wednesday
4. What you do at mealtime
5. ___ blind mice
8. Small
11. Plural of he, she, or it
13. Ham and hamburger are kinds of ___.
15. What you wear on your foot
16. Finished
18. The abbreviation for street
19. ___, myself, and I

Word Families and Representative Words

Lesson 1

ig
big
biggest
dig
pig
rig
wig

ib
bib
rib
sibling

in
chin
fin
pin
tin

Lesson 2

ip
chip
dip
hip
lip
rip
ship
tip
zip

im
dim
him
Jim

it
bit
fit
hit
limit
sit

Lesson 3

is
his
is
sister
this
visit

id
bid

did
hid
kid
lid
rid

ick
chicken
pick
sick
thick
tick

Lesson 4

ich
rich
sandwich
which

itch
ditch
itch
kitchen
pitch
stitch
switch
witch

ix
fix
mix
six

ish
dish
finish
fish
fishing
wish
wishes

Lesson 5

ing
being
bring
doing
going
king
ring
sing
sting
swing
thing
wing

ive
give
live

Lesson 6

iss
dismiss
kiss
miss
missing

iff
cliff
stiff

ill
bill
fill
hill
still

Lesson 7

ut
but
cut
cutting
gut
hut
nut
rut
shut

um
gum
number
sum

up
cup
pups
up
upset

Lesson 8

un
begun
bunch
fun
lunch
run
sun
thunder
under
until

ub
cub
pub
public
rub
rubber
tub

us
bus
dust
just
must
thus
us

Lesson 9

ud
bud
cuddle
huddle
mud
study
sudden

ug
bug
drug
dug
juggle
snuggle
ugly

uck
buck
buckle
duck
luck
struck
stuck
truck
tuck

Lesson 10

uss
cuss
discuss
fuss
muss

uff
bluff
buffalo
cuff

huff
muffin
puff
scuff
stuff

ull
dull
gull
lull
mull
skull

Lesson 11

ush
blush
gush
hush
mush
rush
usher

unk
chunk
drunk
dunk
junk
sunk
trunk

ung
hung
hunger
lung
rung
sung

udge
budge
fudge
judge
nudge

Lesson 12

et
basket
basketball
bet
better
carpet
forget
kettle
market
met

set
settle
ticket

en
Carmen
center
chicken
children
citizen
driven
Ellen
enter
hen
men
pencil
seventy
sudden
twenty
women

eg
beg
begged
begging
leg
peg

Lesson 13

ed
fitted
Fred
gas pedal
hundred
medicine
Ned's
red
shed
Ted
United States
wanted
wedding

Lesson 14

ell
bell
bellhop
fell
hello
jelly
sell
spell
spelling
tell

umbrella
yell
yellow

ess
address
careless
dress
dressing
illness
less
lesson
mess
press
sickness
unless
waitress

Lesson 15

eck
check
checkup
deck
neck
necktie
paycheck
peck
speck

edge
edge
hedge
ledge

ent
absent
bent
cent
different
payment
present
rent
sent

Lesson 16

ot
bottle
cotton
forgot
got
hot
knot
lot

shot
spot

on
bonnet
crayon
donkey
fond
honest
on
onto
pond
upon

ong
along
belong
long
song
strong
wrong

op
bellhop
chop
copper
hop
mop
operator
shopping
stop
top

Lesson 17

ob
Bob
hobby
job
problem
rob
robin

ock
block
clock
flock
lock
o'clock
pocket
rock
sock
stockings

ox
box
fox
ox

Lesson 18

od
fodder
God
nod
rod

odge
dodge
hodge-podge
lodge

Lesson 19

at
at
attic
bat
battery
battle
cat
cattle
hat
matter
Saturday
scatter
that's

an
an
animal
can
Canada
cannot
Dan
janitor
January
man

ab
absent
cab
cabbage
cabin
cabinet
grab
rabbit
tablet

as
as
gas
gas pedal
gas tank
has
hasn't

master
pasture

Lesson 20

ad
admit
bad
glad
had
lad
ladder
mad
radish
sad
saddle
shadow
want ads

am
damage
exam
examination
family
grammar
ham
hamburger
hammer
Pam
program
Sam
Sam's

ag
bag
drag
flag
rag
tag
wagon

ap
apple
application
clap
happen
happy
lap
map
nap
napkin
road map
slap
snap

Lesson 21

ax
ax

lax
relax
tax

Lesson 20

ack
back
backwards
black
crack
cracker
lack
pack
rack
sack
shack
snack
track

ask
ask
mask
masking tape
task

ang
angry
hang
language
rang
sang

Lesson 22

ass
bass
brass
class
classified
glass
grass
mass
pass

ash
ash
bash
cash
cashier
dash
mash

atch
catch
hatch
latch
match
patch
scratch

ath
bath
math
path

Sight Words

Sight Word	Lesson Number	Sight Word	Lesson Number	Sight Word	Lesson Number	Sight Word	Lesson Number
about	10	five	2	or	5	Wednesday	15
after	13	for	4	orange	20	were	2
again	9	forty	22	over	21	what	7
against	9	four	1	part-time	18	when	14
am	2	Friday	15	pay	15	where	7
and	4	full	11	pull	11	while	14
any	9	full-time	18	purple	20	white	20
apartment	17	girl	14	put	8	who	4
Apt.	17	go	5	Rd.	17	whom	11
are	1	goes	8	red	20	with	4
ate	19	gone	11	road	17	would	7
Ave.	17	grade	18	said	8	yellow	20
avenue	17	gray	20	Saturday	15	yesterday	19
be	2	green	20	says	7	yet	5
because	13	hate	19	separated	16	you	3
before	13	have	6	seven	2	your	6
behind	21	he	2	shall	11		
beside	21	her	3	she	2		
between	21	high school	18	shoe	11		
black	20	if	6	should	7		
blue	20	in	21	single	16		
boy	14	into	21	six	2		
brown	20	is	1	sixty	22		
but	5	laugh	9	so	5		
buy	9	lettuce	12	some	6		
by	4	like	19	St.	17		
car	12	listen	12	stop	12		
care	14	little	10	street	17		
Co.	18	love	10	Sunday	15		
come	5	male	16	ten	3		
company	18	married	16	that	10		
could	5	me	3	the	1		
date	19	meat	19	there	10		
did	13	milk	12	they	3		
diploma	18	Miss	16	thirty	22		
divorced	16	Monday	15	three	1		
do	4	Mr.	16	through	21		
does	4	Mrs.	16	Thursday	15		
done	8	Ms.	16	to	6		
Dr.	17	nine	3	today	19		
drive	17	ninety	22	too	9		
eat	19	no	5	Tuesday	15		
egg	12	none	8	twelve	3		
eight	2	not	13	two	1		
eighty	22	o'clock	15	under	4		
elementary school	18	of	4	until	13		
eleven	3	on	21	use	14		
eye	10	once	7	want	6		
female	16	one	1	was	2		
fifty	22	only	8	we	3		